PRENTICE-HALL FOUNDATIONS OF MODERN *Genetics* SERIES

Sigmund R. Suskind and Philip E. Hartman, Editors

AGRICULTURAL GENETICS *James L. Brewbaker*

GENE ACTION *Philip E. Hartman and Sigmund R. Suskind*

EXTRACHROMOSOMAL INHERITANCE *John L. Jinks*

DEVELOPMENTAL GENETICS* *Clement Markert*

HUMAN GENETICS *Victor A. McKusick*

POPULATION GENETICS AND EVOLUTION *Lawrence E. Mettler*

THE MECHANICS OF INHERITANCE *Franklin W. Stahl*

CYTOGENETICS *Carl P. Swanson, Timothy Merz, and William J. Young*

* Published jointly in Prentice-Hall's *Developmental Biology Series*

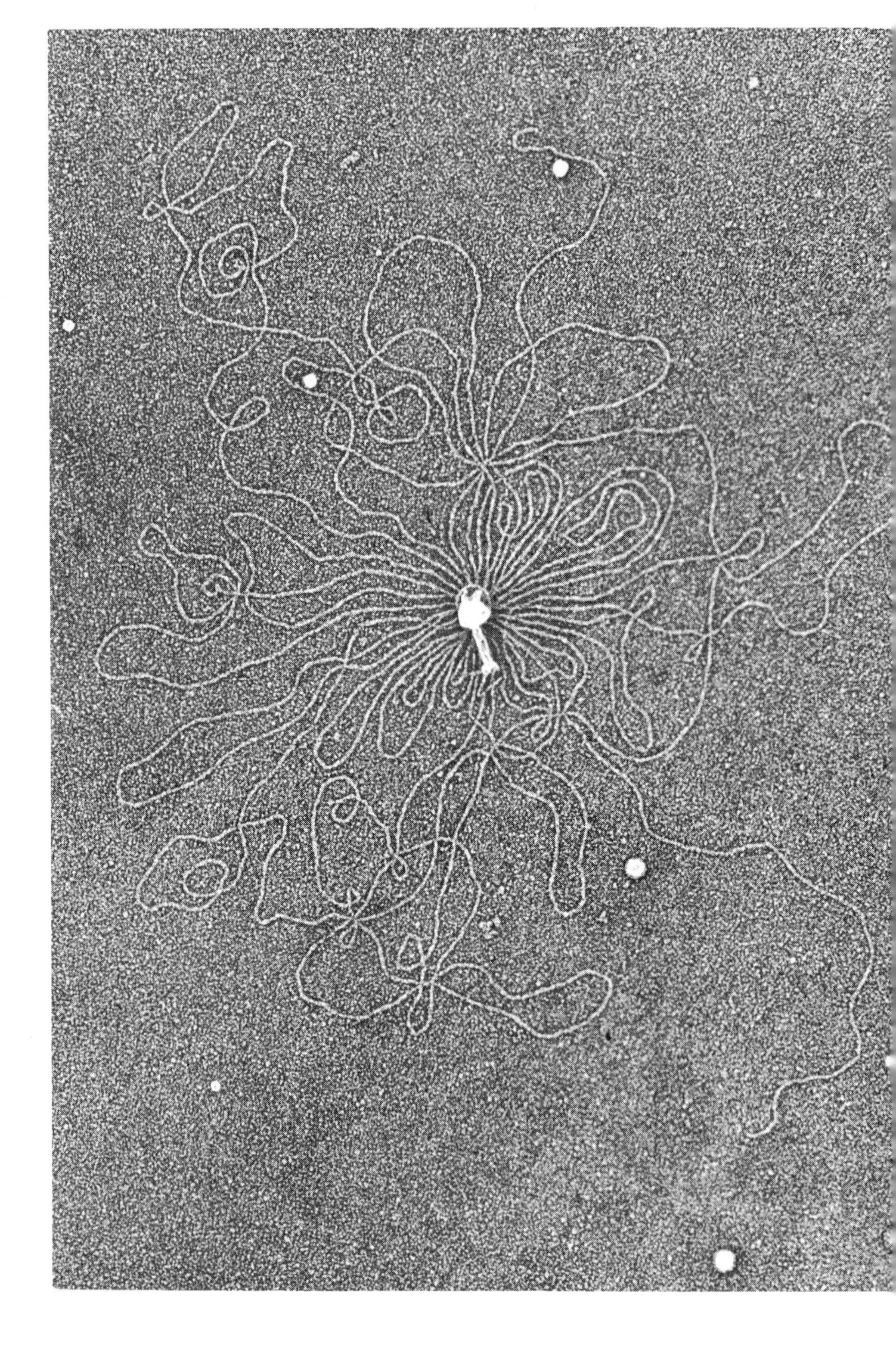

THE MECHANICS OF INHERITANCE

Franklin W. Stahl

University of Oregon

Prentice-Hall, Inc. Englewood Cliffs, New Jersey

Second printing.......... February, 1965

FOUNDATIONS OF MODERN GENETICS SERIES

Printed in the United States of America
Library of Congress Catalog Card Number: 64-16042

The Mechanics of Inheritance
C-57102-P C-57103-C

Frontispiece. The protein coat of a bacterial virus lying on the DNA experimentally released from it. The photograph, kindly supplied by A. K. Kleinschmidt, appeared in *Biochim. Biophys. Acta, 61* (1962), 857. Magnification: 66,000×.

PRENTICE-HALL INTERNATIONAL, INC., *London*
PRENTICE-HALL OF AUSTRALIA, PTY., LTD., *Sydney*
PRENTICE-HALL OF CANADA, LTD., *Toronto*
PRENTICE-HALL OF INDIA (PRIVATE) LTD., *New Delhi*
PRENTICE-HALL OF JAPAN, INC., *Tokyo*
PRENTICE-HALL DE MEXICO, S.A., *Mexico City*

This book was written for Andy and Josh;
all their friends are welcome to read it, of course.

Foundations of Modern Genetics

Genetic research is alive with excitement and revolutionary advances. Important to the development of science and to the evolution of social structure, genetic thought is widening its impact on many areas: immunology, protein chemistry, cellular physiology, developmental biology, medicine, agriculture, and industry.

So many partnerships and such rapidly expanding methodology demand a fresh approach to genetic training—an approach attempted in this series.

The basic principles of genetics are few and simple. We present them with enough description of accessory scientific areas to allow comprehension not only of the principles themselves but also of the types of experiments from which the concepts have evolved. Such an approach compels the reader to ask: What is the *evidence* for this concept? What are its *limitations?* What are its *applications?*

The Prentice-Hall Foundations of Modern Genetics Series presents the evidence upon which *current* genetic thought is based. It is neither a history nor a survey of all genetic knowledge. The short volumes make possible a stimulating, selective treatment of the various aspects of genetics at the intermediate level, and sectional divisions allow free choice of emphasis in differently oriented college genetics courses.

The references cited in each volume and the current research literature are the immediate sequels to this series, but the true sequel remains in the hands of the alert reader. He will find here the seed of more than one enigma, the solution of which he, himself, may help bring into man's comprehension sometime in the future.

SIGMUND R. SUSKIND
PHILIP E. HARTMAN

McCollum-Pratt Institute
The Johns Hopkins University

Preface

To a degree scientific textbooks can be revised to stay abreast of the evolution of our knowledge. However, there occasionally comes to an area of science a major "breakthrough," a new discovery (experimental or theoretical) that permits one to look upon the area with a new perspective. Old texts then must go to the shelf (not the wastebasket, please) and new ones to the students' desk tops. The newer texts may or may not be "better" than the older ones, but the succession is as inevitable as the discoveries that force it.

Since 1953, genetics has been growing explosively in response to the light shed upon it by the elucidation of the chemical structure of the genic material. The trip to the shelf for the standard introductory genetics texts is now overdue. It is only this realization that has given me courage to participate in the preparation of a series that I sincerely hope will be up to the task of replacing (or supplementing) the genetics texts currently in use.

I think that *this* volume can be engaged at three levels. *Readers* who want a view of primary genetic concepts should gain it from a few evenings in an armchair. *Pupils* who need a familiarity with these concepts might find it through working the problems at the ends of chapters (tackle the Appendix early!). I hope that *students* will find this book, its companion volumes, and the reading suggested to be helpful in their search for understanding of life on earth.

A number of friends have helped me with tactical problems by criticizing various versions of the manuscript; they include Alexander Weinstein, Gert and Jon Weil, Mary Louise Eagleson, Burt Guttman, Jette Foss, Eric Terzaghi, George Streisinger, Mary Stahl, Joyce Emrich, Maury Fox, Rollin Hotchkiss, and Aaron Novick, and the series editors (also and still my friends), Sig Suskind and Phil Hartman. Whatever degree of clarity I have achieved in the text is due to their help. The obscurities that remain are mine, as is the strategy employed in this introduction to transmission genetics. I am sure that the strategy chosen will appear of dubious value to some; its adoption unavoidably led me to slight many important advances in knowledge of the physics and chemistry of DNA (the "genic material") while sullying the formal purity of Mendelian[1] genetics by acknowledging others.

I owe a special debt to Dr. James Kezer, who prepared the special section, the Appendix to Chapter 7, on meiosis in salamanders. He has supplemented his beautiful photographs, previously unpublished, with a descriptive text of outstanding clarity.

F.W.S.

[1] Adjective referring to the nineteenth century Austrian who established most of the ideas this book aims to elucidate.

Contents

Heredity

One of man's routine observations is that cats give birth to cats. Cats have been up to this for centuries all the world over. Furthermore, there is no documented instance of a cat giving birth to anything else. This is the primary observation of the science of heredity.

Similarly, by rather simple observations, one can conclude that Douglas firs produce seed that germinate to give only Douglas firs. The fruit fly, *Drosophila,* has been watched by the world's great geneticists since 1910; it has never given birth to other than *Drosophila.* Cats and firs are likewise the object of genetic research. They do have the advantage of being prettier than flies, but they share with *Drosophila* two major disadvantages as objects of study. They are big (requiring lots of lab space), and they are slow to reproduce (requiring lots of lab time).

These familiar creatures possess in common another feature—their developmental cycles are sufficiently complicated that an analysis of their heredity requires a simultaneous understanding of *all* the basic principles of genetics. One objective of this series is to provide the basis for such an analysis, and this volume has been written with that goal in mind. The primary aim of this volume, however, is to focus on the physical basis of inheritance, and that goal is better served by an examination of the revealing experiments on heredity in microorganisms.

Microorganisms in genetic research

A number of factors have contributed to the success of these experiments. The microorganisms are small (requiring little lab space) and fast (requiring little lab time). In addition, the developmental cycle of each microorganism is sufficiently simple that the basic principles of genetics can be conveniently illustrated one at a time. On the other hand, when considered collectively, microorganisms provide sufficient diversity to permit step-by-step illustration of the features of more complicated systems.

Let us look at the microorganisms that will carry us through this first chapter.

Fig. 1.1. A stereo-electron photomicrograph of a pair of bacterial cells representing two different strains of *Escherichia coli*. The pair of cells is engaged in sexual conjugation (see Chapter 6); one of the cells is being pestered to death by bacteriophage particles (see Chapter 2). A three-dimensional view of the whole show can be perceived, after a little effort, if you hold the book about two feet from your eyes and stare at the figure for a moment or two. If this doesn't work, try putting one end of a piece of paper between the photomicrographs and the other end against your nose, so that you see only one picture with each eye. This photo was kindly supplied by the photographer, Thomas F. Anderson.

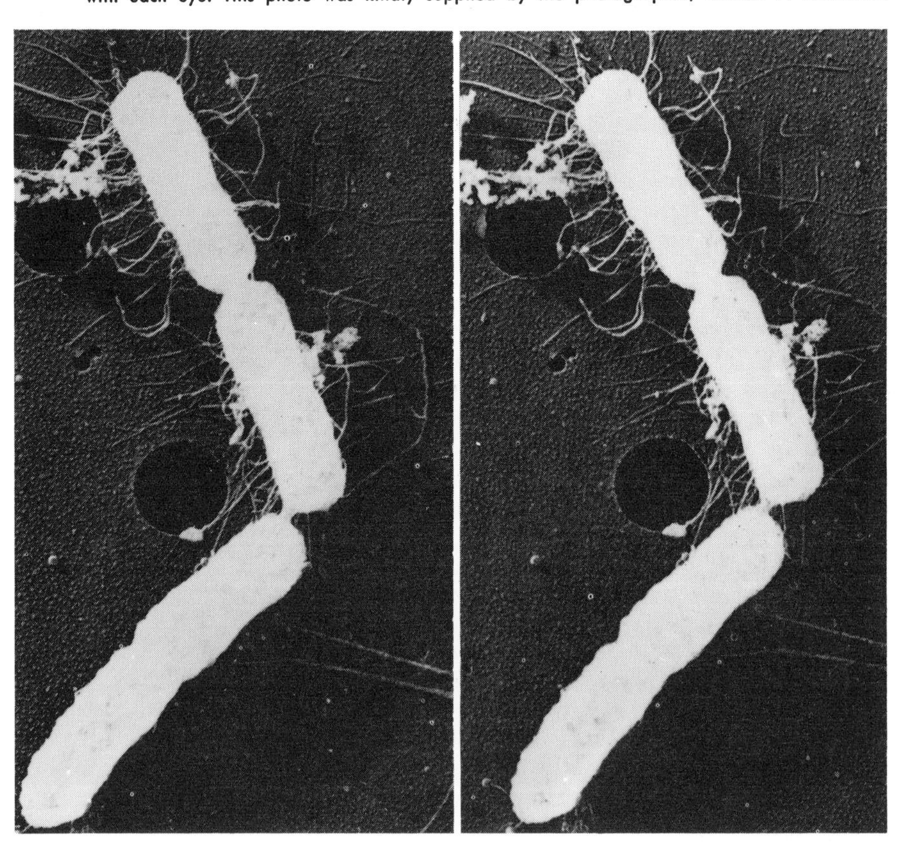

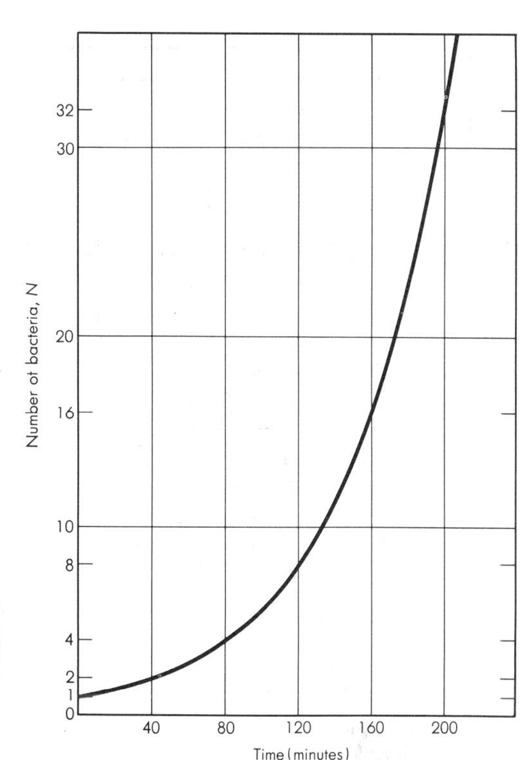

Fig. 1.2. The number of cells in an actively dividing bacterial culture as a function of time. In an actively dividing culture, the number of bacterial cells increases at a rate proportional to the number of cells present at any moment.

In 1946, E. L. Tatum wrote (in *Cold Spring Harbor Symposia on Quantitative Biology*): "the bacteria, with their biochemical and physiological versatility, ease of cultivation and study . . . may prove excellent material for the study of the fundamental problems of . . . genetics. . . . The main attribute lacking in bacteria . . . is their apparent lack of a sexual phase, the existence of which would permit their examination by classical genetic methods for the segregation of characters as Mendelian units." We shall see in subsequent chapters that bacteria are not only free of this defect, but that, on the contrary, they are superb material for the study of "Mendelian units." At present, we shall entertain them for their earliest recognized virtues.

The growth of bacterial cultures

A bacterium reproduces itself in an apparently simple fashion: it elongates, then splits transversely into two bacteria; after a suitable interval, each of the daughter bacteria reproduces similarly. We can plot the number of bacteria as a function of time in a culture maintained under constant, favorable conditions (Fig. 1.2). We see that a doubling every 40 minutes, for instance, leads to a thousand fold increase in about 400 minutes.

The relationship between the number N of bacteria in a culture and the number of times the population has doubled is written as

$$N = N_0 2^g \qquad \text{(Eq. 1.1)}$$

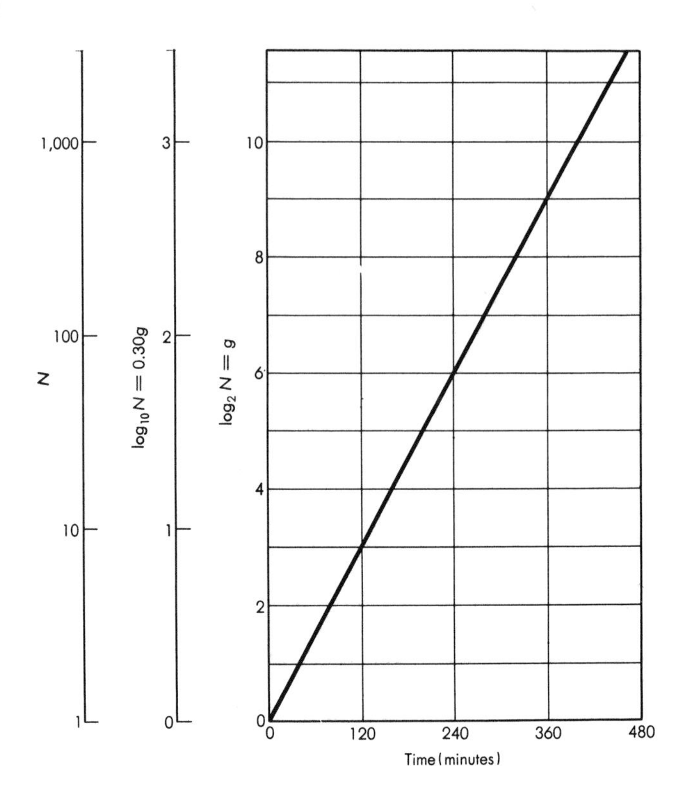

Fig. 1.3. The logarithm of the number of cells in an actively dividing bacterial culture as a function of time. A plot of log number of cells versus time is linear for an actively dividing culture.

where N_0 is the number of bacteria present at time zero and g is the number of generations (population doublings) that have occurred. An actively dividing culture maintained under constant conditions multiplies at a constant rate, so that

$$g = kt \qquad \text{(Eq. 1.2)}$$

where t is time and k is a growth-rate constant.

The consequences of this mode and tempo of reproduction are more easily seen from a plot of the logarithm of the number of bacteria as a function of time (Fig. 1.3). The linear relationship between time and the log number of bacteria (Fig. 1.3) is easy to extrapolate to times beyond those represented on the graph. When multiplication proceeds at the indicated rate of one doubling each forty minutes, after twenty-two hours the initial bacterium has given rise to a population of greater than ten billion individuals, more than three times the number in the human population of the earth.

The bacterium *Escherichia coli* is the type most exploited in the genetics laboratory. It displays the simple growth habit described above, but when subjected to chemical analysis it proves to be about as complicated as any creature. The principal classes of compounds found in *E. coli* are listed in Fig. 1.4b. This array of chemicals, which characterizes each of the billions of individuals in a culture, is to be contrasted with the handful of simple compounds (Fig. 1.4a) that must be present in the culture medium in order for *E. coli* to duplicate. These few compounds provide sources of each of the chemical elements out of which a bacterium is composed and, in addition, a source of energy to drive synthetic reactions. *E. coli* (like any other organism) can arrange the atoms in the compounds available to it into a biochemical and morphological likeness of itself, and it does so at a rate that permits it to duplicate 1.5 times per hour. The myriad chemical conversions carried out by *E. coli* (for instance) can proceed at this speed because they are catalyzed by enzymes.

Mutation in bacterial cultures

E. coli gives rise upon duplication to more *E. coli* as faithfully as cats, firs, and flies perpetuate their kind. The faithfulness of this reproduction on the morphological level reflects its faithfulness on the enzymatic level. A typical (wild-type) *E. coli* can grow in the simple culture medium shown in Fig. 1.4a, can utilize the sugar lactose as an energy source, and cannot grow in the presence of the antibiotic penicillin. The reproductive fidelity of such typical cells can be challenged by experiment. In such an experiment, a number of wild-type cells are introduced into a culture medium in which all of their descendants can grow even if they lack one of the three qualities characterizing the wild type. The medium contains no penicillin, contains a variety of energy sources, and contains most of the biochemicals of which a *coli* cell is composed. The culture is incubated until millions or billions of cells are present. These cells are then tested for the three properties by which the wild type is characterized.

The cells are easily studied with respect to the reproductive fidelity of the penicillin-sensitivity character. The total number of bacteria in the culture can be estimated by distributing a measured, appropriately diluted volume of the culture on the surface of a nutrient medium solidified with agar. After incubation of the nutrient-agar plate each bacterium has given rise by successive duplications to a clone of bacteria. (A clone is that assemblage of individuals to which a bacterium, or any other creature, has given rise by successive duplications.) The cells in each clone remain clustered together in a colony around the point at which the initial bacterium of the clone was deposited. By counting the colonies, which are easily visible after overnight incubation, the number of cells deposited is determined. From the known dilution and the volume plated, the number of bacteria in the culture can be estimated. The number of penicillin-resistant cells in the culture can be estimated by plating on nutrient agar containing penicillin. We shall define the frequency of penicillin-resistant variants in the culture as (number of resistant bacteria) / (total number of bacteria).

The frequency of variants unable to ferment lactose (lactose-negative variants) can be measured by plating a fraction of the culture on a medium containing lactose and a dye that changes color in the immediate vicinity of colonies that are fermenting lactose.

In each of the procedures above, the frequency of variants in a culture is estimated by counting colonies. Thus the variants that are

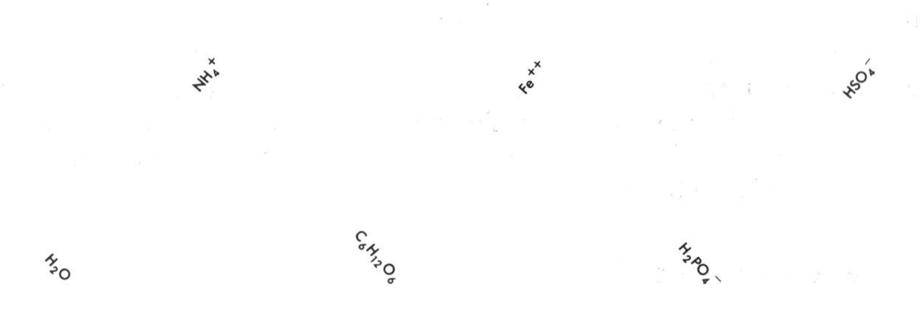

Fig. 1.4a. The constituents of a simple growth medium that supports active division of the bacterium *Escherichia coli* at a rate of 1 generation each 40 minutes at 37°C.

Fig. 1.4b. Some of the more interesting chemical compounds in a bacterial cell. See William D. McElroy's *Cell Physiology and Biochemistry*, 2nd ed. (Prentice-Hall, 1964) for a full discussion of the significance of these constituents of cells.

ENZYMES Hundreds of different proteins, each of which is a specific polymer of twenty different AMINO ACIDS

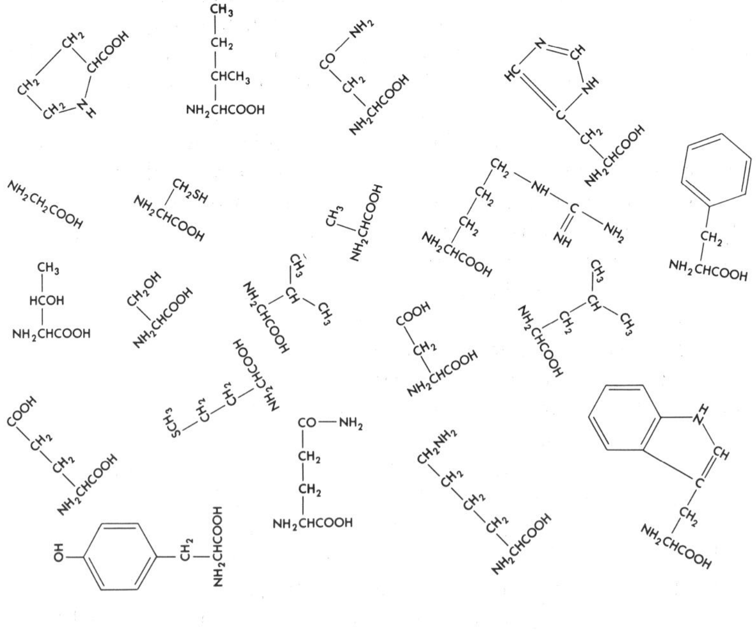

CO-ENZYMES Dozens of different kinds of molecules that participate in enzyme-catalyzed reactions, e.g.,

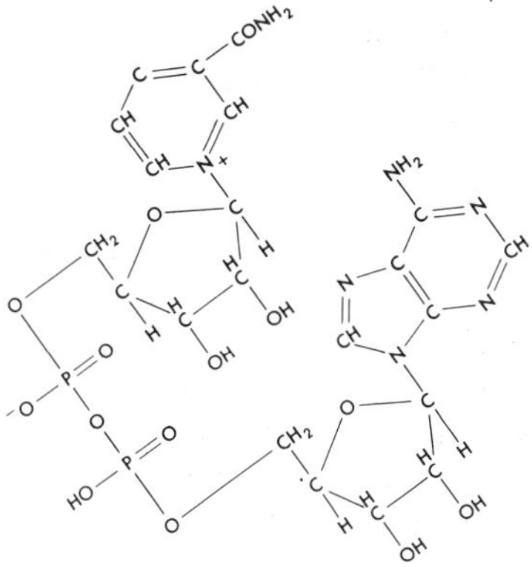

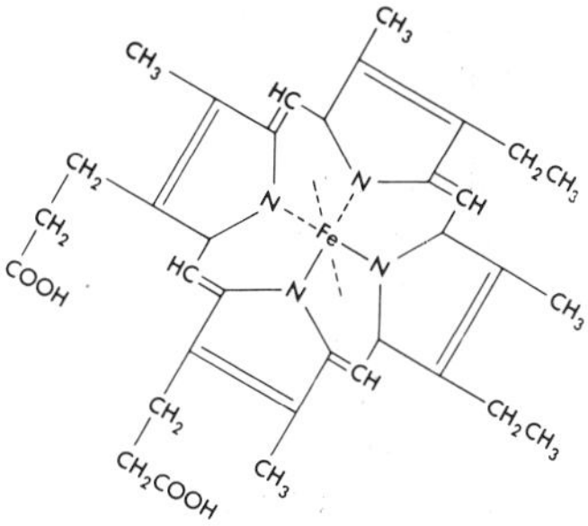

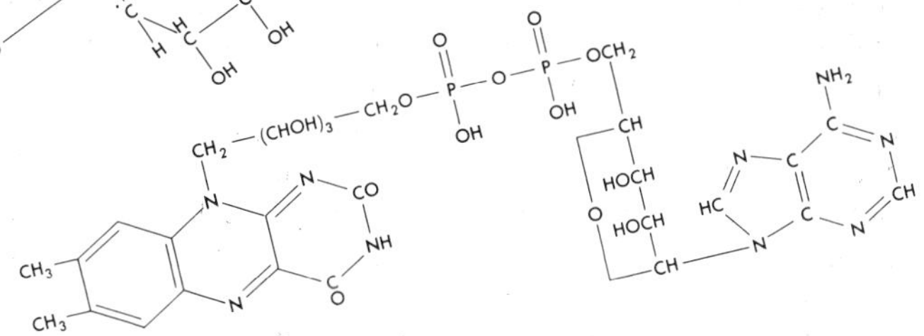

NUCLEIC ACIDS Are classifiable into two types (DNA and RNA), both of which are polymers containing a 5-carbon sugar, phosphorus, and four (or more) different NITROGENOUS BASES

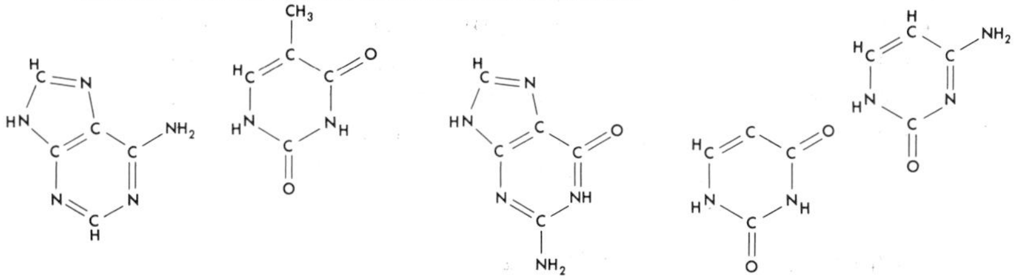

"STRUCTURAL MATERIALS" The cell wall of *E. coli* is composed of several polymers, e.g.,

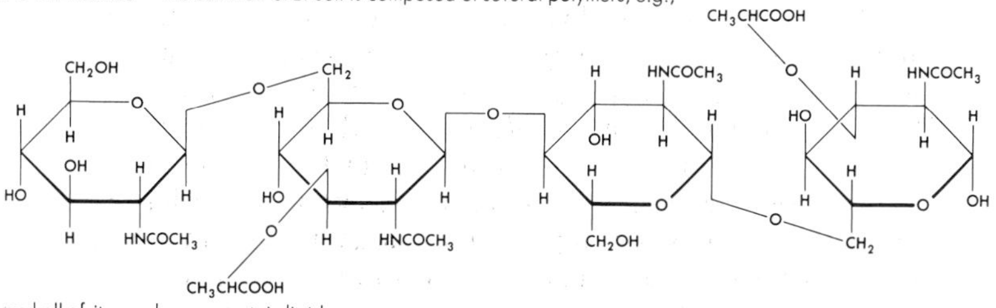

and all of its membranes contain lipids, e.g.,

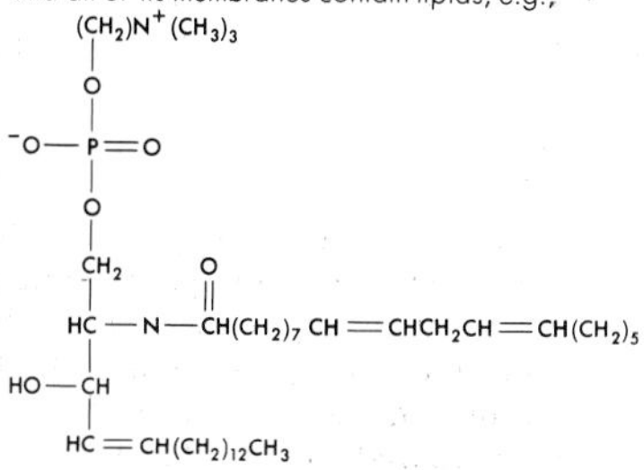

studied are those which, upon duplication, give rise to variant cells like themselves; they are mutants.

Testing a culture for the frequency of mutants unable to grow on simple culture medium is more difficult. The "replica-plating" method of Joshua Lederberg can be applied to this case to ease the labor. About one hundred cells from the culture are plated on a medium of the same properties as the liquid one in which the culture was prepared. The plate is incubated until each cell gives rise to a visible colony. Members of each of the colonies are then transferred to another plate. The transfer is conveniently accomplished, without losing track of the identity of each colony, with the aid of a tautly held piece of velveteen. The velveteen is pressed first against the master plate containing the colonies and then against the other (replica) plate. The replica plate, which contains the simple medium described in Fig. 1.4a, is then incubated to permit the formation of visible colonies. The typical outcome of this experiment is that the replica plate has colonies corresponding to each of the colonies on the master plate. Thus each of the hundred cells spread on the master plate has the same simple nutritional requirements as the wild-type cell with which the liquid culture was originally inoculated.

If replication is carried out on a number of master plates, however, the result is not invariably the same. An occasional colony fails to replicate, indicating that the growth requirements of its members are not met by the simple medium in the replica plate (Fig. 1.5). An assiduous application of this technique can provide a measure of the frequency of auxotrophic (nutritionally defective) mutants in a culture of prototrophic (nutritionally wild-type) cells.

Measurement of mutation rate

The frequency of variant individuals in a population of organisms is determined by many factors. Together with their interactions, these factors are the primary subject matter of Lawrence Mettler's *Population Genetics and Evolution,* another volume in this series. At this point we are interested in only one of them—the mutation rate.

The mutant frequency in a culture grown from an inoculum of nonmutant cells bears a simple relationship to the mutation rate, the probability per bacterium per division of undergoing mutation.

If we assume the mutation rate to a particular mutant type to be constant per act of duplication, then we can define mutation rate to that type by the equation

$$\Delta m_g = aN_g \qquad \text{(Eq. 1.3)}^1$$

[1] This and subsequent equations employ a mathematics suitable for synchronously dividing populations. This approach exchanges but a bit of accuracy for a lot of clarity. Three assumptions usually justifiable in such experiments are made: (1) Mutant and wild-type bacteria duplicate at equal rates under the conditions employed. (2) The rate of mutation from mutant to wild type is not large compared to the rate of mutation a from wild type to mutant. (3) The total number of mutants for the character under observation is small compared to the total population size.

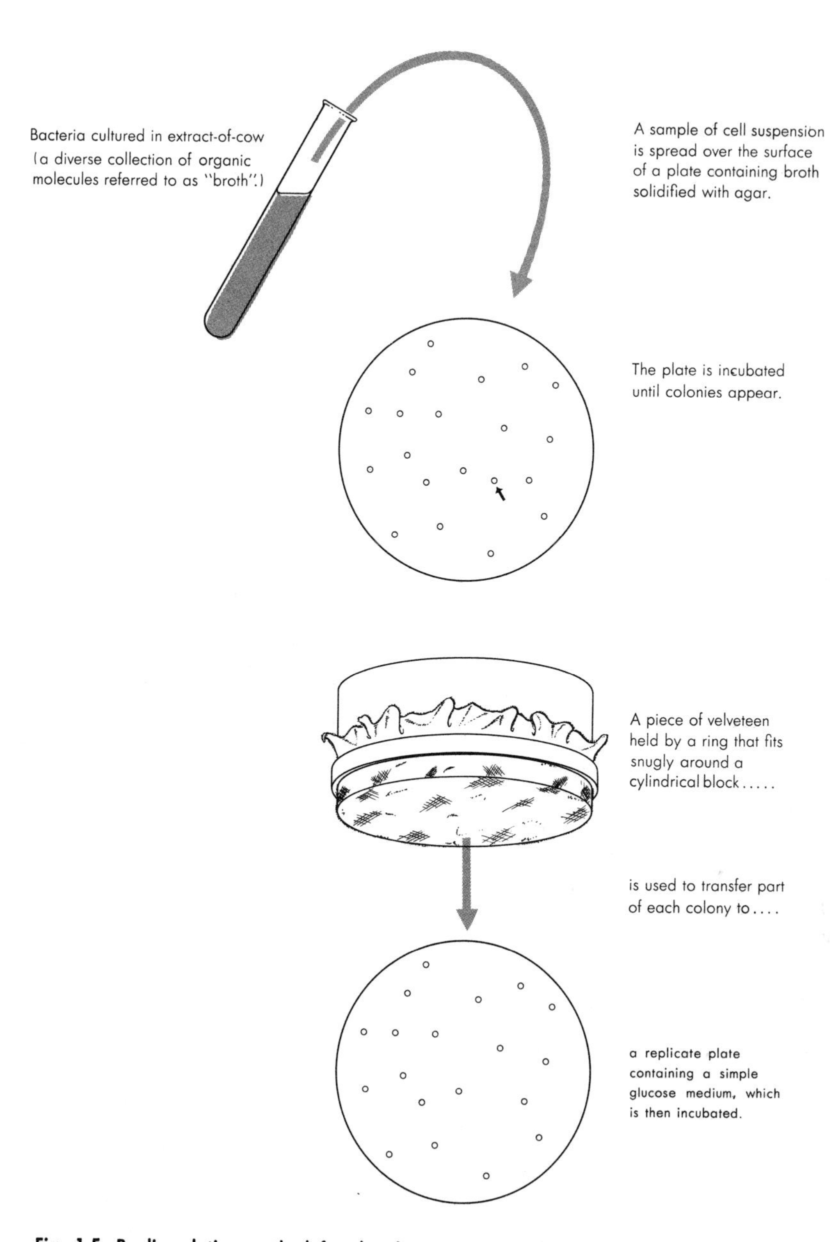

Fig. 1.5. Replica-plating method for the detection and isolation of mutants unable to grow on simple growth medium. A hundred or so cells from a broth culture of bacteria are spread on a broth medium solidified with agar. After overnight incubation each cell has given rise to a visible colony. A tautly held piece of velveteen is pressed lightly against the plate and then against the surface of a sterile plate containing simple glucose medium solidified with agar. The second plate is incubated until visible colonies appear. The colonies on this replica plate arise in positions corresponding to the positions of the colonies on the master plate. Occasional colonies that fail to replicate (such as the one indicated by the small arrow) are nutritionally defective mutants (auxotrophs).

where Δm_g is the number of mutants Δm newly arising in generation g and aN_g is the mutation rate a times the number of bacteria N present at generation g.

If we assay a culture at generation g, the mutants will include those that arose in that generation *plus* the descendants of those that arose in previous generations. The number of mutations occurring in generation $g - 1$ is

$$\Delta m_{g-1} = aN_{g-1} \quad \text{(Eq. 1.4)}$$

Since

$$N_{g-1} = \frac{N_g}{2}$$

$$\Delta m_{g-1} = \frac{aN_g}{2} \quad \text{(Eq. 1.5)}$$

Each mutant arising in generation $g - 1$ will have duplicated once by generation g so that the number of mutants at generation g descended from mutants arising at generation $g - 1$ is

$$\rho_{g-1} = \frac{2aN_g}{2} = aN_g \quad \text{(Eq. 1.6)}$$

We see that at generation g, the number of mutants newly arisen (Eq. 1.3) is equal to the number of mutants descended from mutants arising at generation $g - 1$. On the average, the contribution to the mutant population at generation g from mutations occurring in prior generations is the same for each generation. Thus, on the average, the number of mutants in the culture is

$$\rho = gaN_g \quad \text{(Eq. 1.7a)}$$

and the frequency of mutants is

$$\frac{\rho}{N_g} = ga \quad \text{(Eq. 1.7b)}$$

In a series of identical cultures started from small inocula, mutations will, by chance, occur earlier in some than in others. Mutations occurring quite early give rise to large clones of mutants. Therefore, such early events, although rare, contribute heavily to ρ. In any given set of a few cultures, however, the earliest possible events are unlikely to occur. Therefore, Eq. 1.7a predicts a higher average number of mutants than is apt to be observed. By the same token, the application of Eq. 1.7a to estimates of mutation rate a is likely to lead to an underestimate. Equation 1.8 was derived by S. E. Luria and Max Delbrück to describe the *likely* observed average number of mutants in a series of C identical cultures.

$$r = aN_g \log_2 CaN_g \quad \text{(Eq. 1.8)}$$

Mutation rates for various characters are generally found to be low, most of them manifesting reproductive infidelity in far less than one duplicative act per 10,000.

Mutations and enzymes

When mutant cells are detected, isolated, and cultivated, their offspring retain the mutant characteristics with a fidelity as great as and often greater than that manifested by the wild type. Mutant cultures can then be examined biochemically to determine what alterations in their enzyme content are responsible for their new properties. A mutant isolate unable to grow on simple medium may be found to lack the enzyme that catalyzes a known step in the production of a necessary cellular constituent, e.g., the conversion of citrulline to the amino acid arginine (Fig. 1.6). The penicillin-resistant mutant may be found to contain, in contrast to the wild type, an enzyme that can degrade penicillin to a harmless substance (Fig. 1.7). The mutant strain that cannot ferment lactose may be found to lack the enzyme that hydrolyzes the disaccharide into two monosaccharides—the first degradative step in its utilization as an energy source (Fig. 1.8).

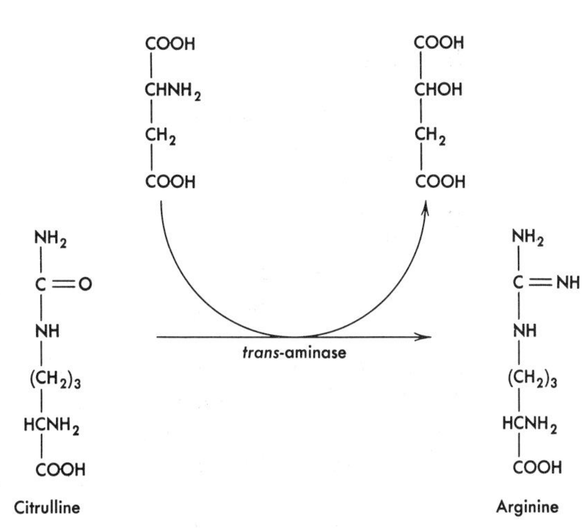

Fig. 1.6. Mutants that fail to synthesize enzymatically active molecules of the proper *trans*-aminase cannot make arginine, an amino acid required for protein synthesis.

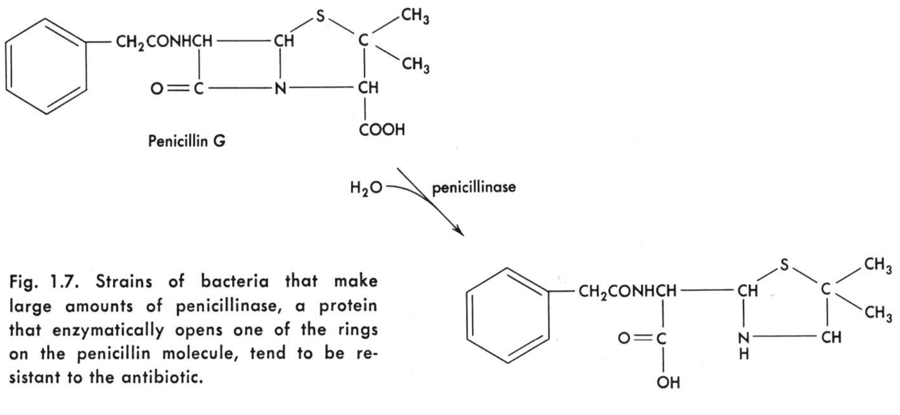

Penicillin G

H_2O penicillinase

Fig. 1.7. Strains of bacteria that make large amounts of penicillinase, a protein that enzymatically opens one of the rings on the penicillin molecule, tend to be resistant to the antibiotic.

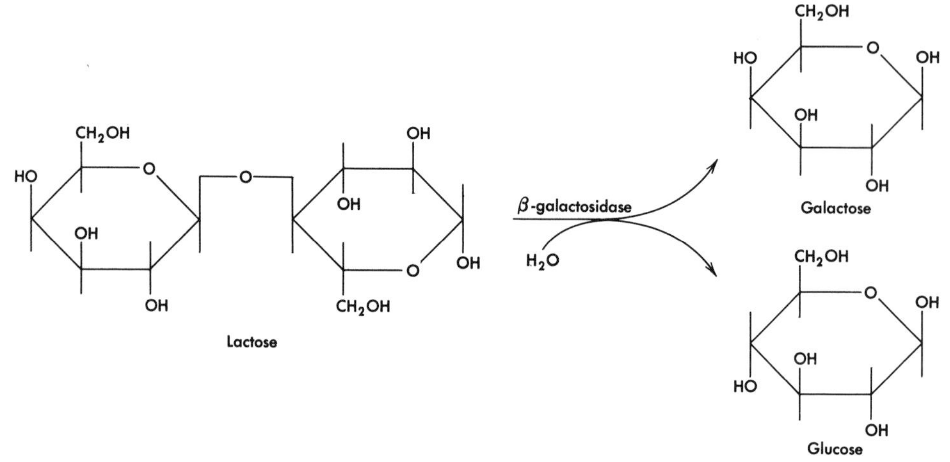

Fig. 1.8. The disaccharide lactose can be hydrolytically cleaved to galactose and glucose by the enzyme β-galactosidase. Mutants that fail to make this protein, or make an inactive form of it, cannot ferment lactose.

Summary

Three properties of living things are illustrated by the foregoing discussion: (1) The reproduction of living things is faithful, but (2) not perfectly faithful. Mutations occur. (3) Many of these mutations alter one of the enzymes of the creature or prevent its appearance. Indeed, only those mutations that *do* change the biochemical capacities of the creature are significant to the creature and detectable to us.

From these considerations a wise (or naïve) philosopher might build an argument for the existence within living things of a set of instructions with three properties: (1) The instructions are reproduced. (2) The instructions are occasionally altered. (3) The instructions dictate the construction of proteins.

The next chapter will examine experiments that identify a substance ("genic material") present within bacteria and other creatures and responsible for their remarkable reproductive fidelity as well as for their occasional lapses.

References

Lederberg, Joshua, and Esther Marilyn Lederberg, "Replica Plating and Indirect Selection of Bacterial Mutants," *J. Bacteriol., 63* (1952), 399-406. Reprinted in *Papers on Bacterial Genetics,* Edward A. Adelberg, ed. (Boston: Little, Brown & Co., 1960), pp. 24-31. A description of the technique and several applications of the replica plating method.

Luria, S. E., and Max Delbrück, "Mutations of Bacteria from Virus Sensitivity to Virus Resistance," *Genetics, 28* (1943), 491-511. Reprinted in *Papers on Bacterial Genetics,* pp. 3-23. The mathematical basis for the analysis of mutation in bacterial cultures.

McElroy, William D., *Cell Physiology and Biochemistry,* 2nd ed. Englewood Cliffs, N.J.: Prentice-Hall, Inc., 1964. An efficient review of cellular biochemistry at the beginning level.

Monod, Jacques, *Recherches sur la croissance des cultures bacteriennes*. Paris: Hermann, 1942. Improve your ability to read French while enjoying this light classic on the growth of bacterial cultures.

Problems

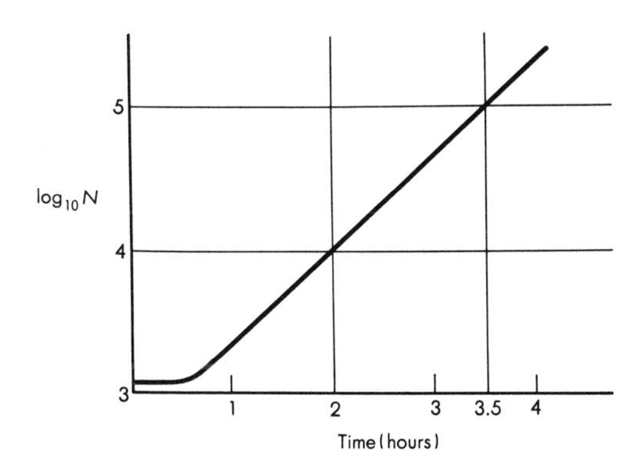

1.1. The graph depicts the increase in the number of cells in a bacterial culture following inoculation of the nutrient-broth medium with 1.5×10^3 cells from an "old" culture. After a "lag" of about a half hour, the culture becomes "actively dividing." For the portion of the curve that is exponential, we define the generation time as the time within which the population exactly doubles in size. Calculate the generation time for the growth curve depicted.

1.2. Suppose we inoculate 100 ml. of broth with 1,000 actively dividing cells each of bacterial strain A and strain B. A few hours later we observe 5×10^5 per ml. of strain A and 5×10^3 per ml. of strain B. What are the relative growth rates of the two strains?

1.3. Liquid bacterial growth medium in a sterile tube was inoculated with actively multiplying bacteria. Call the time of inoculation time-zero. The culture was assayed for the number of bacteria each hour thereafter. The data are tabulated below.

Time	*Cells*
0	3.0×10^5
1	8.0×10^5
2	2.0×10^6
3	5.3×10^6
4	1.4×10^7
5	3.6×10^7
6	9.4×10^7
7	2.5×10^8

(a) On a sheet of graph paper plot log (number of bacteria) versus time.

(b) What is the time required for the number of cells to double?
(c) Suppose there were *no* mutants (of a specified type) in the inoculum. When the number of bacteria reached 1.2×10^6, the frequency of mutants was measured and found to be 10^{-4}. *How many* mutant cells would you expect to find when the number of cells reached 2.4×10^6? (Assume a negligible rate of back mutation and equal viability of the mutant and wild type.)
(d) What is the value of the mutation rate?

1.4. Each of 10^6 tubes was inoculated with 1 penicillin-sensitive cell. Growth then proceeded in perfect synchrony. When there were 1,024 cells in each tube, the tubes were examined for penicillin-resistant cells. 1,000 of the tubes had at least 1 resistant cell. On the assumption that penicillin resistance arises by mutation, how many tubes would you expect to find with *exactly* 1 resistant cell? 2 resistant cells? 4 resistant cells? more than 4 resistant cells?

1.5. Once upon a time, 10^5 streptomycin-sensitive *Staphylococcus* cells were deposited randomly upon the surface of nutrient agar in each of 3 petri dishes. The dishes were incubated for several hours. At the end of that time 10 ml. of liquid were placed on the agar surface in dish 1; the surface of agar under the liquid was scraped; and the liquid, containing essentially all the cells from the dish well dispersed, was assayed for number of cells. The cell concentration was found to be 1.3×10^6 cells/ml. At the same time, dish 2 was sprayed with streptomycin, and dish 3 was respread thoroughly and then sprayed with streptomycin. After overnight incubation, 128 colonies appeared on dish 2.
(a) What is the most likely number of colonies to be found in dish 3, assuming a mutational basis for streptomycin resistance?
(b) Calculate, from these results, the mutation rate to streptomycin resistance.

1.6. In a series of 10 "identical" cultures grown from small inocula to a total of 10^8 cells each, there was observed an *average* of 2 drug-resistant cells per culture. What is the estimate of mutation rate to drug resistance given by this result? (Eq. 1.8 and a piece of graph paper will help you reach the answer to this one.)

1.7. Each of 100 identical tubes of growth medium was inoculated with about 10^4 streptomycin-sensitive bacterial cells. When the cultures reached 10^8, they were examined for the presence of streptomycin-resistant cells. 87 of the tubes contained at least 1 such cell.
(a) What was the average number of mutations per tube? (The probability that any particular cell undergoes mutation is very small; the total number of *opportunities* for mutation is very large. The Poisson distribution—see the Appendix—can be employed in the analysis of this problem. Of the terms P_n of the distribution, the information for determining P_0 is provided by the problem. An estimate of x, the average number of "successes" per series of N trials, can, therefore, be obtained.)
(b) Calculate the mutation rate (approximately) to streptomycin resistance. (From Eq. 1.3 and the growth equation, Eq. 1.1, determine a relationship between m, the average number of mutations per tube, N_g, the final population size, and a, the mutation rate.)

Identification of the Genic Material

The series of experiments that led to the identification of the genic material can be said to have begun about 1920. It was about that time that both bacterial viruses and bacterial transformation were discovered.

Bacterial transformation

Wild-type cells of the pneumococcus bacterium (*Diplococcus pneumoniae*) are encapsulated by a polysaccharide excretion. If such cells are introduced into a susceptible mammal, severe illness usually follows. Occasional mutants devoid of a capsule arise in laboratory cultures of pneumococci. Such mutants are far less virulent than the encapsulated strains; they rarely cause an animal any difficulty. The study of encapsulated and nonencapsulated pneumococci led Frederick Griffith to the discovery in the 1920's of bacterial transformation. Griffith's experiment demonstrating transformation of avirulent bacteria to the virulent type is summarized diagrammatically in Fig. 2.1.

Griffith inoculated one group of mice with avirulent cells, a second group with heat-killed virulent cells, and a third group with both avirulent and heat-killed virulent cells. The first two groups of animals were unaffected by the inoculations. Mice in the last group, however, developed severe septicemia. The interaction within the mice between viable avirulent cells and heat-killed virulent

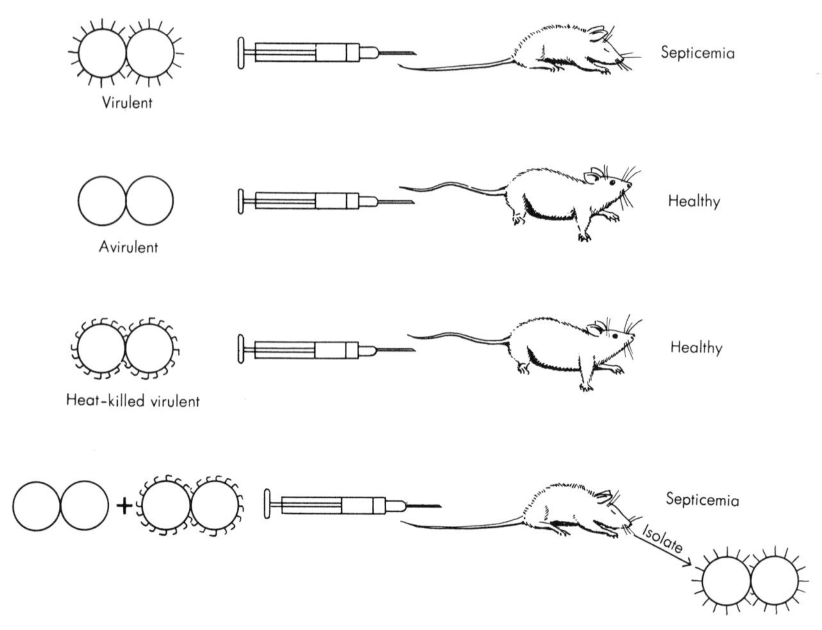

Fig. 2.1. Bacterial transformation in living animals (in vivo). Avirulent cells and heat-killed virulent cells interact in the mouse to produce living virulent cells. This figure is based on Fig. 5 in David M. Bonner's *Heredity* (Prentice-Hall, 1961).

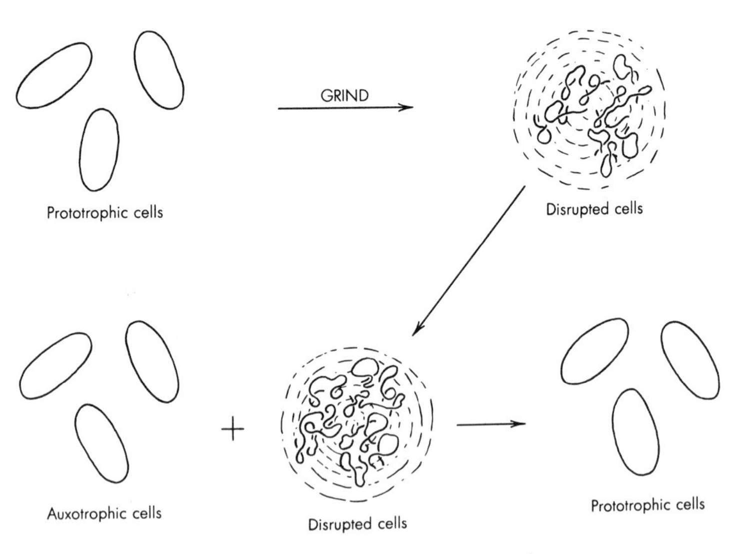

Fig. 2.2. Bacterial transformation in the test tube (in vitro). Debris from cells (*Bacillus subtilis*) capable of growing on a simple medium can transform nutritionally defective (auxotrophic) mutants to prototrophy (state of being hereditarily wild type with respect to nutritional requirements).

cells led to the appearance of viable virulent cells. Two alternative explanations for this result were prominent. (1) The presence of viable avirulent pneumococci restored the heat-killed cells to viability. (2) The heat-killed cells conferred the property of virulence upon the avirulent cells. The latter conclusion is the proper one, but its proof follows most easily from experiments performed subsequently and described below.

A major advance in the study of bacterial transformation came with the demonstration in the early 1930's that transformation can be obtained in vitro. When a nonencapsulated cell population was exposed to the debris from disrupted encapsulated cells, a small fraction of the cells were transformed to the encapsulated virulent type.

In recent years, transformation of a large number and variety of hereditary characters has been demonstrated among different species of bacterium. In many of these cases the character transformed represents the ability to make a protein that functions as an enzyme in the catalysis of an identifiable chemical conversion within the cell. For the case of encapsulation, the presence or absence of a capsule depends directly on the presence or absence of a functioning enzyme required in one of the steps in capsule formation. In the bacterium *Bacillus subtilis* it has been possible to transform each of the types of mutant characters illustrated in Figs. 1.6, 1.7, and 1.8. An in vitro transformation experiment using *B. subtilis* is diagrammed in Fig. 2.2.

Figure 2.2 carries implications for two important properties of transformation. (1) In order to transform cells of, say, type X to type Y (where X and Y are mutually exclusive alternatives), debris from disrupted cells of type Y is required. Cells of type X do not yield debris capable of inducing transformation from X to Y. (2) When the type Y cells derived by transformation multiply, they give rise to more type Y cells. When disrupted, the progeny of transformed cells yield debris that can transform X cells to Y cells; this debris will *not* transform Y cells to X cells.

Transformation has a third fundamental property, which for technical reasons is usually more difficult to demonstrate than are the first two. Transformation can be carried out reciprocally. If debris from type Y cells can transform type X cells to type Y, then debris from type X cells can transform type Y cells to type X.

Each of these three points will be subject to amplification in subsequent chapters. At this point we need to establish only that *transformation involves a specific, directed alteration in a hereditary characteristic of a bacterium.* An elucidation of the mechanism of transformation was certain to have a profound impact on our views of heredity.

Identification of the transforming agent

In 1944, Oswald T. Avery, Colin M. MacLeod, and Maclyn McCarty announced the results of ten years of work in the analysis

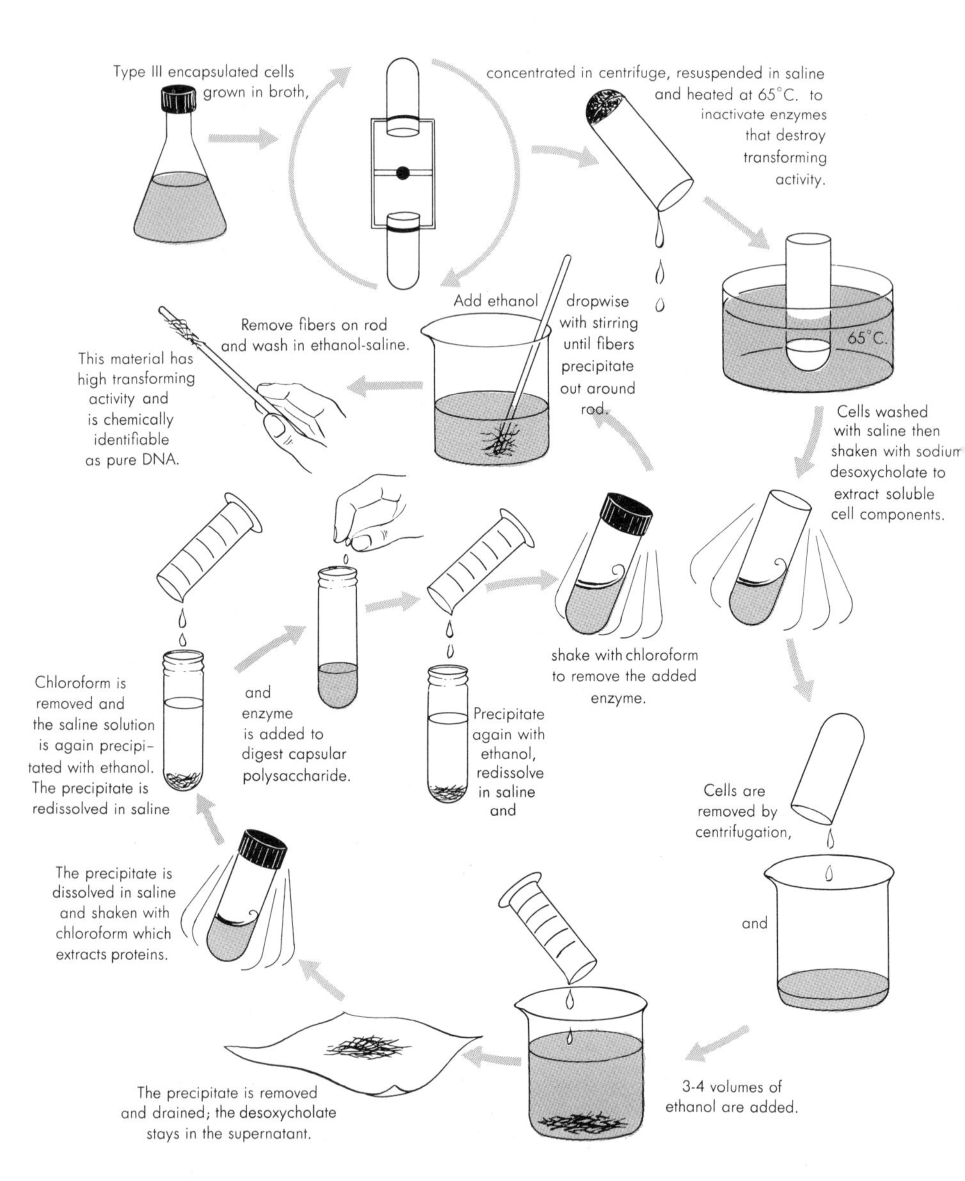

Fig. 2.3. The procedure by which Avery, MacLeod, and McCarty isolated pure DNA with high transforming activity. The DNA derived from cells encapsulated in type III polysaccharide was added to cells of a nonencapsulated strain derived by mutation from type II cells. Some of these cells were transformed by the DNA to the type III encapsulated variety.

of the mechanism of transformation. They fractionated into various chemical species the debris from disrupted encapsulated cells and determined the transforming activity of each. The procedure and outcome of their experiment are outlined in Fig. 2.3.

Only the DNA fraction (see Fig. 1.4b) was found capable of transforming unencapsulated cells to encapsulated cells. Realization of the importance of this demonstration was slow in coming to the genetic community: a change of intellectual climate was perhaps as important as the painstaking improvements in purification and analytic methods in convincing geneticists that transformation was really interesting. The experiment has by now been repeated a multitude of times for the character of encapsulation as well as for many of the other hereditary characteristics that occur in systems amenable to transformation.

Two principal hypotheses were advanced to account for the role of DNA in transformation. One hypothesis supposed that DNA could act somehow upon genic material to produce directed mutations, i.e., to change the genic material of the recipient cells to make it resemble the genic material of the donor cells. The second hypothesis *equated* DNA with the genic material and explained transformation as a transfer of genic material from donor to recipient cells.

The identification of DNA as genic material was further substantiated in an experiment performed on viruses that multiply inside of bacteria (bacteriophage).

The life cycle of bacteriophage T2

Bacteriophages (phages), like other viruses, multiply inside of cells giving rise to more phage particles with a fidelity comparable to that of the cat or the *coli*. About twenty minutes after a bacterium is infected by a phage particle, it bursts open, liberating a few hundred particles identical (usually) to the particle that initiated the infection. The phage T2, which multiplies inside *E. coli*, was used in the experiment that aided in the identification of DNA as genic material.

T2-phage particles are composed of about 50 per cent by mass of protein and 50 per cent DNA. In the early 1950's, A. D. Hershey and Martha C. Chase demonstrated that when a phage infects a bacterium, its DNA enters the host cell, but over 90 per cent of its protein remains attached to the outside surface of the cell. Most of the protein on the outside of the cells can be removed by shear forces vigorously applied throughout a suspension of infected bacteria. (The technical details of this experiment are described in the legend to Fig. 2.4.) Infected bacteria from which the protein moiety of the T2-phage particles had been removed produced a normal crop of T2-phage particles; *the DNA that entered the cell constituted the sole physical thread of hereditary continuity between infecting and emerging particles.*

The Hershey–Chase experiment, when considered together with the observations of many other workers, leads to the picture of a phage

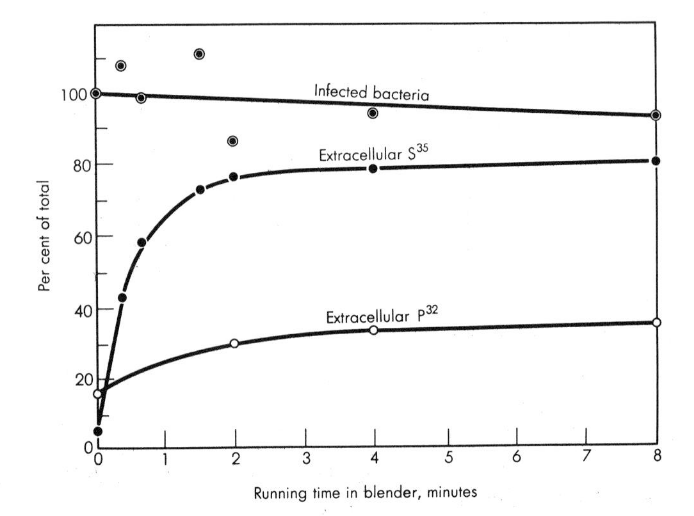

Fig. 2.4. Two batches of phage particles were prepared. One batch was prepared by growing phages in bacteria containing radioactive sulfur (S^{35}); the other batch was prepared in bacteria containing radioactive phosphorus (P^{32}). Since several amino acids contain sulfur but DNA does not, the first batch of phage particles was "labeled" in its protein moiety; since phosphorus is a component of DNA (see Chapter 3) but not of proteins, the second batch was labeled in its DNA. Each batch of phages was permitted to attack bacteria. The infected bacteria were subjected to shear forces in a kitchen blender, and the amount of radioactivity removed from the cells was measured. The S^{35} was easily removed, but the P^{32} was not. The number of infected bacteria that produced a crop of phage particles was diminished by the treatment only slightly, if at all. This figure, reproduced by permission of A.D. Hershey, originally appeared in *J. Gen. Physiol.*, *36* (1952), 47.

infection outlined in Fig. 2.5. The phage particles attach to the bacterium by means of the "tail." The DNA, contained within the head made of protein, enters the cell. Within twenty minutes about two hundred new phage particles are formed complete with DNA and protein "coat." Each of these particles can itself initiate a full cycle of infection if permitted to attack a bacterium.

Life has doublecrossed the text writer—a number of viruses contain no DNA, but are instead made of RNA and protein. (Philip Hartman and Sigmund Suskind's *Gene Action,* another volume in this series, has a lot to say about RNA. At this juncture we need know only that RNA is a close chemical relative to DNA; both are nucleic acids.) For a number of RNA viruses, it has been shown that the RNA portion of the virus alone serves as the genic material. The first demonstration of this fact, performed separately by Heins L. Fraenkel-Conrat and Gerhard Schramm, is diagrammed in Fig. 2.6.

Mutations occur for both DNA and RNA viruses. These mutations are usually detected by their influence upon some stage of the infectious cycle. When the nucleic acid of a mutant particle invades a cell, the progeny particles produced, like the infecting particle, are mutant.

Fig. 2.5. The infectious cycle of a virulent bacteriophage as illustrated by phage T2. The mature particle, shown in longitudinal section, attaches by its tail fibers to a bacterium. The sheath contracts, the core penetrates the cell surface, and the DNA of the particle passes into the bacterium. About twenty minutes later at 37°C. the cell bursts and a few hundred new mature particles are released.

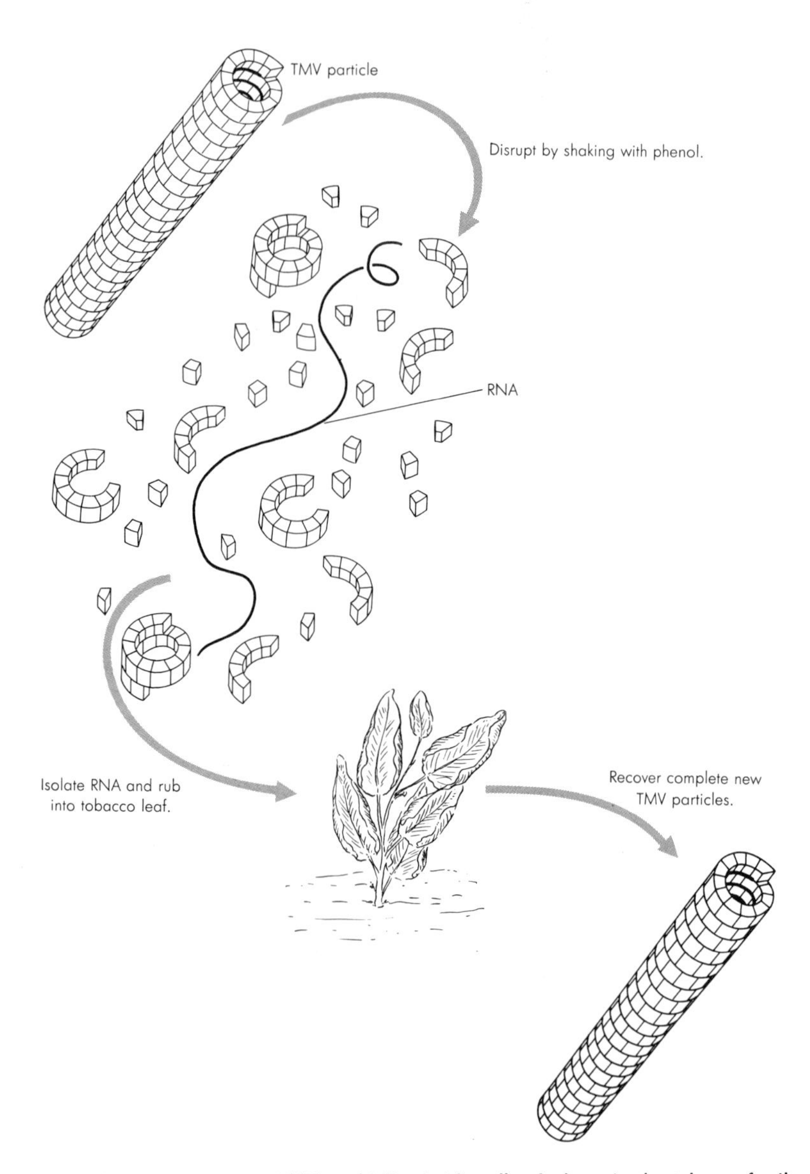

Fig. 2.6. Tobacco mosaic virus (TMV) multiplies inside cells of plants in the tobacco family. The virus particles are rod shaped and are composed of a protein sheath surrounding an RNA core. The protein can be dissociated from the RNA by shaking the particles with water and phenol. The RNA and protein can then be separately tested for their ability to infect tobacco plants. Only the RNA fraction of the virus retains this ability. The plants infected by this RNA produce a crop of complete TMV particles.

Summary

The approaches described in this chapter have been sufficient to establish that DNA is the paramount genic material of many viruses and probably of all bacteria. Indeed, it is a well-accepted hypothesis of genetics that DNA plays its genic role in any organism in which it is present. (The evidence in support of this view will emerge by implication in subsequent chapters, especially in Chapters 4-6.) DNA is found in all the examined organisms on the earth, with the exception, previously described, of some viruses.

Chapter 3 will look at the chemical structure of DNA and, parenthetically, at RNA.

References

Avery, Oswald T., Colin M. MacLeod, and Maclyn McCarty, "Studies on the Chemical Nature of the Substance Inducing Transformation of Pneumococcal Types," *J. Exp. Med., 79* (1944), 137-58. Reprinted in *Classic Papers in Genetics,* J. A. Peters, ed. (Englewood Cliffs, N.J.: Prentice-Hall, Inc., 1959), pp. 173-92, and in *Papers on Bacterial Genetics,* Edward A. Adelberg, ed. (Boston: Little, Brown & Co., 1960), pp. 147-68. The beauty of the experiments is equaled by the clarity of the exposition.

Fraenkel-Conrat, Heins L., and Robley C. Williams, "Reconstitution of Tobacco Mosaic Virus from Its Inactive Protein and Nucleic Acid Components," *Proc. Nat. Acad. Sci. U.S., 41* (1955), 690-98. Reprinted in *Classic Papers in Genetics,* pp. 264-71. TMV that has been dissociated into its noninfectious protein and its slightly infectious RNA components can be reconstituted in vitro.

Hershey, A. D., and Martha C. Chase, "Independent Functions of Viral Protein and Nucleic Acid in Growth of Bacteriophage," *J. Gen. Physiol., 36* (1952), 39-56. Reprinted in *Papers on Bacterial Viruses,* G. S. Stent, ed. (Boston: Little, Brown & Co., 1960), pp. 87-104. "The experiments reported in this paper show that one of the first steps in the growth of T2 is the release from its protein coat of the nucleic acid of the virus particle, after which the bulk of the sulfur-containing protein has no further function." (From the authors' introduction.)

Lerman, L. S., and L. J. Tolmach, "Cellular Incorporation of DNA Accompanying Transformation in *Pneumococcus,*" *Biochim. Biophys. Acta., 26* (1957), 68-82. Reprinted in *Papers on Bacterial Genetics,* pp. 177-91. An examination of early steps in transformation.

Ravin, A. W., "The Genetics of Transformation," *Adv. Genet., 10* (1961), 61-163. A comprehensive, if not always clear, review of bacterial transformation.

Weidel, Wolfhard, *Virus.* Ann Arbor: University of Michigan Press, 1959. A gentle introduction to the life cycle of bacteriophages.

Problems

2.1. The number of atoms of a given radioisotope that decay per time unit is a constant fraction of the number of undecayed atoms present. The kinetics of such a first order reaction may be written as

$$N = N_0 e^{-kt}$$

where t is time
N_0 is the number of radioactive atoms present at $t = 0$
k is the fraction of atoms decaying in a stated short interval of time (the instantaneous rate of decay)
N is the number of radioactive atoms remaining at time t

For the radioisotope P^{32}, half of the atoms decay in two weeks.
(a) For P^{32} what is the value of k per second?
(b) If your Geiger counter for detecting disintegrations registers on the average once per 11.4 P^{32} decays, how many P^{32} atoms must you have to count 5 counts per second?

2.2. A streptomycin-resistant strain of pneumococcus was grown in a medium containing one P^{32} atom per 20,000 ordinary (P^{31}) atoms. Since DNA contains phosphorus (see Chapter 3), the transforming DNA isolated from the culture was radioactive. If we assume that the bacteria were unable to discriminate between the two isotopes, then we know the fraction of radioactive P atoms in the isolated DNA.
(a) Suppose a sample of the isolated DNA was found to register at the rate of 5×10^3 counts/second/microgram of DNA on your Geiger counter (the one in Problem 2.1b). What fraction of the mass of DNA is phosphorus? One atom of P^{31} has a mass of 5×10^{-23} gm, or 31/Avogadro's number.
(b) Suppose that in a transformation experiment, streptomycin-sensitive cells were mixed with the DNA from Problem 2.2a. Five minutes after mixing, the cells were removed from the mixture, washed, and the radioactivity was measured with a Geiger counter. It was found that a sample of 2×10^7 cells gave 2 counts per second. How many micrograms of DNA were bound per cell?
(c) In units of molecular weight (daltons), how much DNA was bound per cell? (Independent physical studies indicate that DNA as usually isolated has a molecular weight in this range. Transformation experiments are often carried out in the range of one added DNA molecule per cell.)

2.3. The phage T2 contains about 2×10^{-17} gm. phosphorus per particle.
(a) How many phosphorus atoms are contained in each T2 particle?
(b) In units of molecular weight, how much DNA is in each particle if we assume an elemental composition the same as that of pneumococcus DNA? (In Chapter 3 we shall see that this assumption is only approximately true.)

The Structure of DNA (and RNA)

DNA (*d*eoxyribo*n*ucleic *a*cid) usually occurs in nature as long, unbranched, polymeric molecules (Fig. 3.1). A DNA molecule is composed of an intimately associated pair of DNA chains. Each DNA chain commonly is composed of four kinds of monomers. This chapter examines the chemical structure of these monomers, the nature of their linkage into chains, and the nature of the association of pairs of chains with each other. The problem of solving the DNA structure was primarily a physicochemical one. We shall see in Chapters 4 and 5, however, that its solution was the genetic coup of our times.

The deoxyribonucleotides

The monomers out of which a DNA chain is composed are called nucleotides or, more specifically, deoxyribonucleotides. Each nucleotide is a compound of phosphoric acid, the 5-carbon sugar deoxyribose, and one or another of the four kinds of nitrogenous bases. The phosphoric acid and deoxyribose are combined by an ester linkage. For our present purposes we may consider the linkage to be at the number 5 carbon atom of the deoxyribose (Fig. 3.2). The nitrogenous bases, whose structural formulas are shown and identified in Fig. 3.3, are each linked to a deoxyribose at the number 1 carbon atom of the sugar. The structural formulas of the various nucleotides are shown in Fig. 3.4.

Fig. 3.1. An electron micrograph of part of a DNA molecule. A DNA molecule is 20 Å wide and terribly long. This photograph was kindly supplied by Michael Beer. Magnification 100,000×.

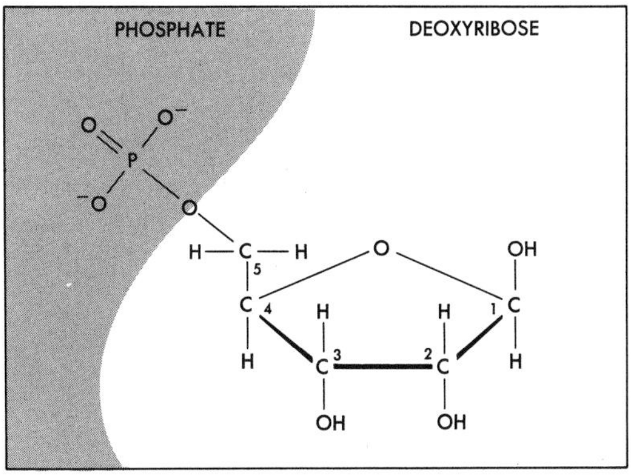

Fig. 3.2. Deoxyribose phosphate. The "backbone" of a DNA chain is a polymer of deoxyribose phosphate.

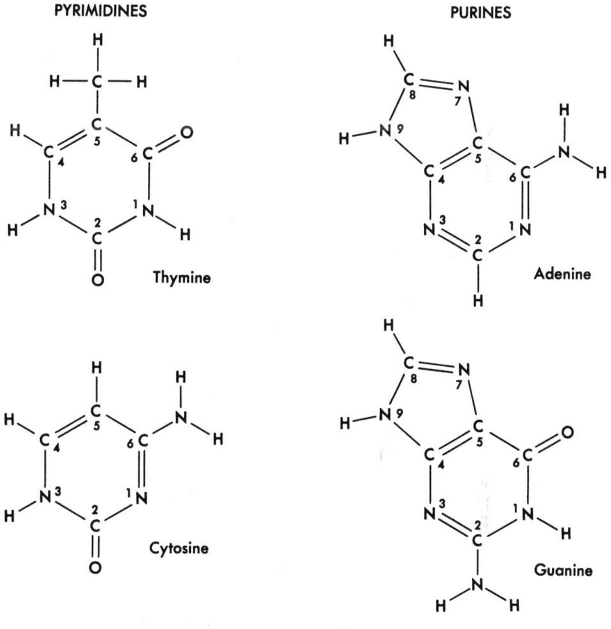

Fig. 3.3. The four nitrogenous bases most commonly found in DNA. The two pyrimidines have a common heterocyclic ring "nucleus" as do the two purines.

DNA chains

In a DNA chain, the nucleotides are linked to each other by ester bonds between the phosphate group of each nucleotide and the number 3 carbon in the deoxyribose of the adjacent nucleotide. A short stretch of a DNA chain showing five nucleotides selected willy-nilly is diagrammed in Fig. 3.5. A DNA chain can be thought of as having a sugar-phosphate "backbone" (on the left in Fig. 3.5) to which is attached at each level one or another of the nitrogenous bases. In nature, DNA chains have various lengths. Some chains are thought to be composed of 200,000 nucleotides; longer ones probably exist.

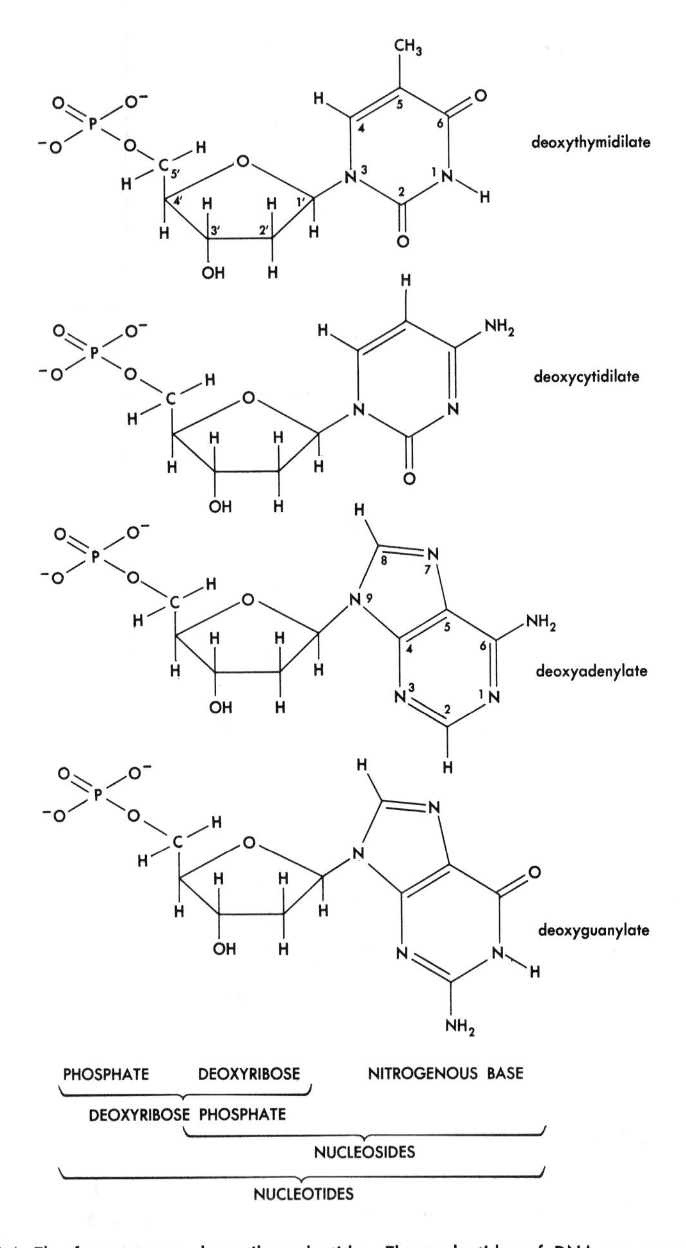

Fig. 3.4. The four common deoxyribonucleotides. The nucleotides of DNA are composed of the nitrogenous bases each attached to deoxyribose phosphate. A nucleotide devoid of its phosphate is called a nucleoside. Each of the nitrogenous bases is attached to deoxyribose by a bond that connects a ring-nitrogen atom of the base to the number 1 atom of the deoxyribose. This latter ring position is often referred to as the number 1′ position of the nucleoside. Henceforth we shall use one of the conventional symbolisms of the organic chemist: carbon atoms in ring structures are implied by a bond angle.

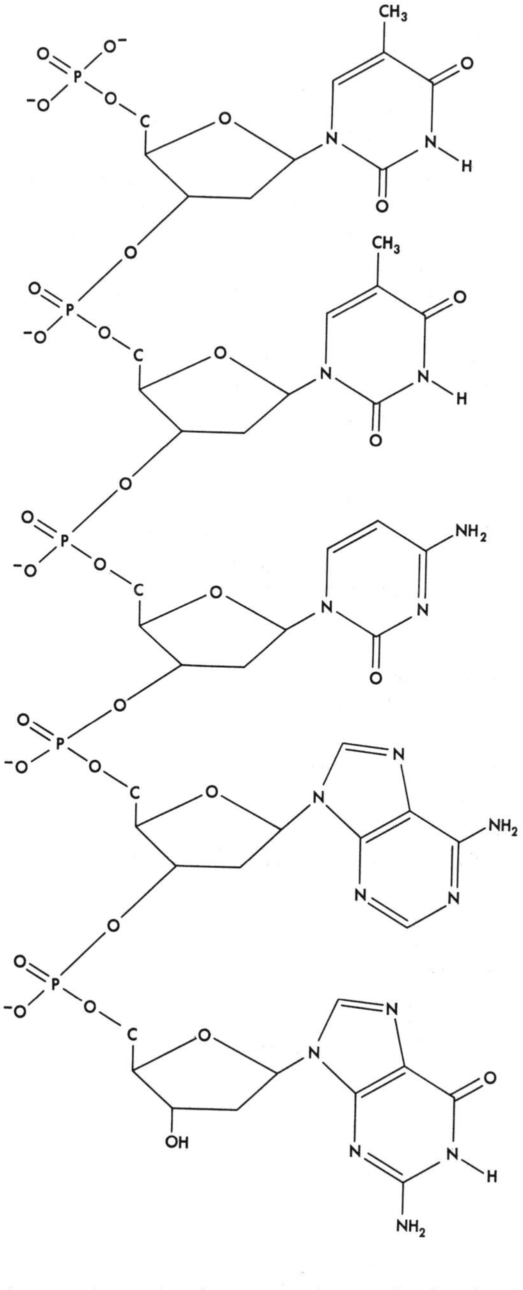

Fig. 3.5. A stretch of DNA with a nucleotide sequence chosen willy-nilly. The nucleosides are connected by phosphate "bridges" that run from the 5′ position of one nucleoside to the 3′ position of the next. In this figure, and henceforth, we adopt another convention of the organic chemist: H's are left out of the structural formulas unless there is a reason for drawing attention to them.

DNA molecules

DNA molecules consist of two chains twisted about each other. There are about ten nucleotides in each chain for each complete turn of the double helix. Each nucleotide in a chain is oriented with its nitrogenous base toward the other chain and its phosphate group away from the other chain. The two chains are held together by hydrogen bonds formed between bases that occupy the same level on the two chains. It is necessary now, and for much of the later material, to understand hydrogen bonding as it can occur between pairs of nucleotides.

A hydrogen bond results from the sharing by two atoms of a single hydrogen atom. (Such a bond may be likened in some degree to the covalent bond that results from the sharing of orbital electrons, but it is far weaker.) In a hydrogen bond, one participating atom acts as a hydrogen donor and the other as a hydrogen acceptor. Each of the nitrogenous bases contains donor atoms and acceptor atoms. Thus, a great variety of hydrogen-bonding arrangements between pairs of bases is possible. In a normal DNA molecule, however, there are restrictions imposed upon the hydrogen-bond interactions between bases. These restrictions are dictated to some extent by the rules of formation of the covalent bonds that join the bases to the deoxyribose and that unite the nucleotides to each other along the sugar-phosphate backbone. Additional restrictions are imposed by three observations. (1) All the base pairs are hydrogen bonded. (2) The sugar-phosphate backbones form a very regular double helix. (3) The planes of the bases are perpendicular to the long axis of the molecule. These three considerations limit to two the number of base-pair associations that can (normally) occur in a DNA molecule. These are shown in Fig. 3.6.

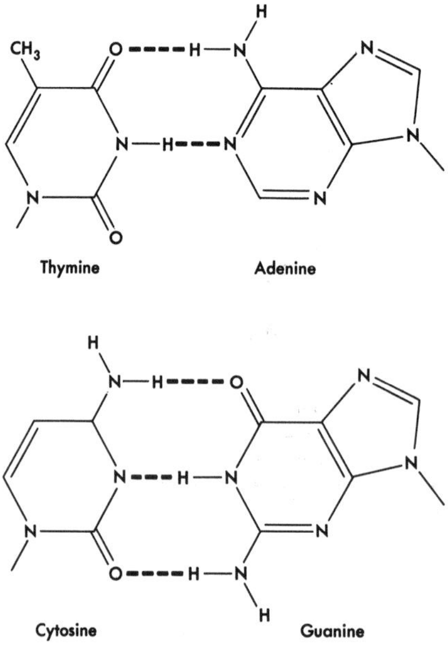

Fig. 3.6. Hydrogen bonding between bases as it occurs in DNA. Of the various hydrogen-bonding interactions that can occur among bases, only these two normally occur in DNA.

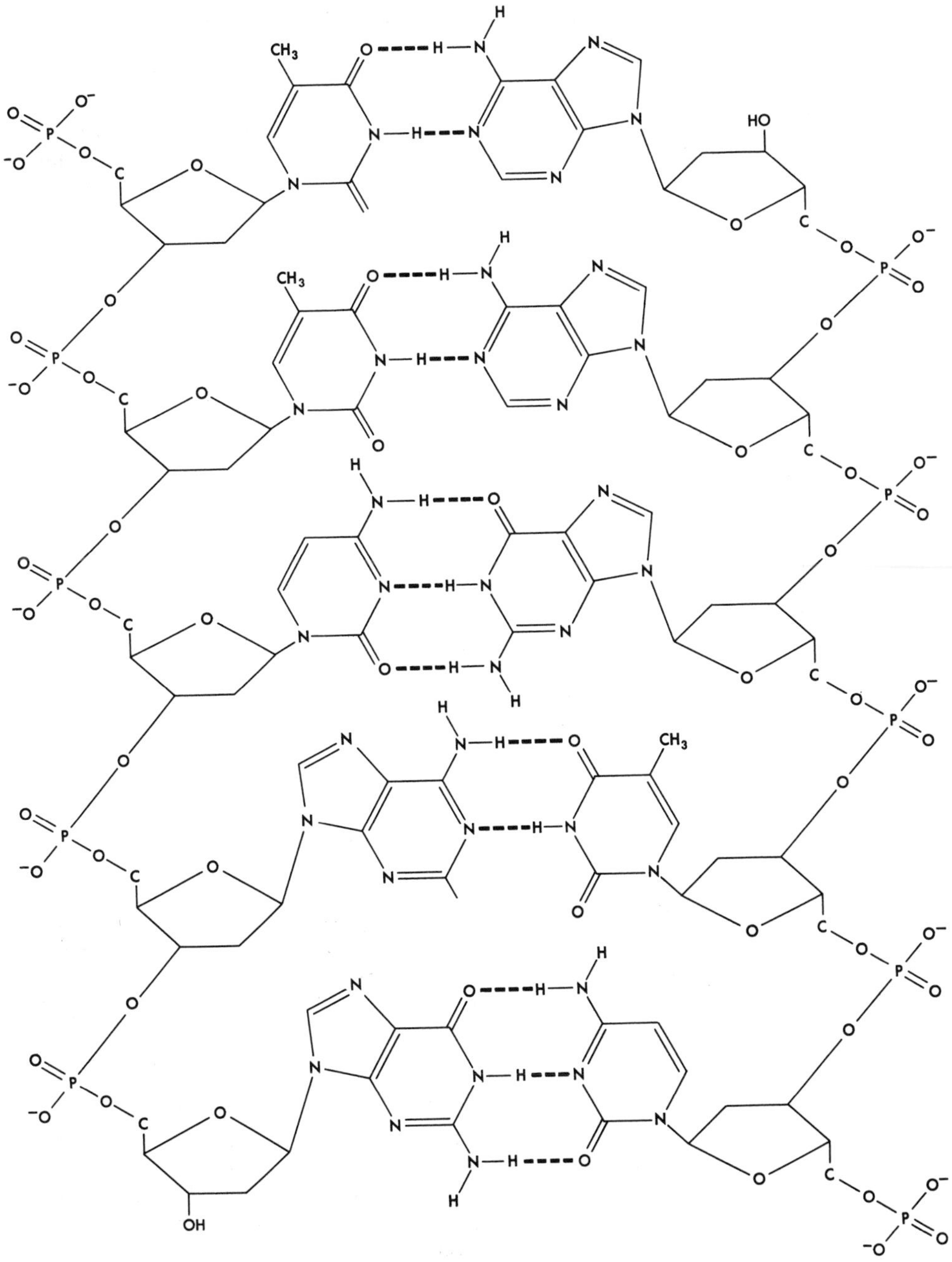

Fig. 3.7. A stretch of a DNA molecule. The chain on the left has the same willy-nilly base sequence shown in Fig. 3.5. The chain on the right has a base sequence complementary to it. The two chains, whose "backbones" run in opposite directions, are held together by hydrogen bonds between the bases. The molecule is further stabilized by its helical nature; the chains are twisted about each other with one twist for each ten nucleotide pairs.

A diagrammatic representation of the structural formula for a short stretch of a DNA molecule is shown in Fig. 3.7. The same willy-nilly base sequence used in Fig. 3.5 is shown with the half twist in the stretch of molecule "ironed out" to simplify the representation. A diagrammatic representation of a stretch of DNA, complete with twist, is shown in Fig. 3.8.

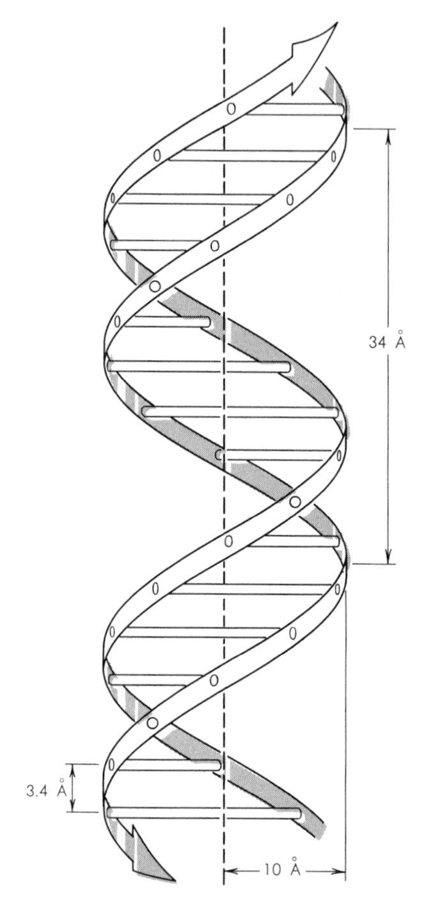

Fig. 3.8. A schematic representation of a DNA molecule. The relationship of the two hydrogen-bonded chains to each other and to the helix axis is illustrated and the basic physical parameters of the model are given.

The solution of the structure of DNA was made possible by the work of hosts of chemists and physicists. The data that permitted the final assembly of this host-collected host of facts were obtained by Maurice Wilkins and his collaborators and by R. E. Franklin and R. G. Gosling. They used the technique of X-ray diffraction, which can, with rather severe limitations, give indications of the spatial arrangements of some of the atoms within a large molecule. Because of the limitations in the technique, X-ray diffraction data of DNA needed lots of interpreting; James D. Watson and Francis H. C. Crick performed that job. The essential accuracy of their interpretation has been attested to repeatedly by the acquisition of more and better diffraction data. Other observations, described below, have strengthened our belief in the validity of the Watson–Crick structure for DNA.

A feature of the Watson–Crick model for DNA is that at any level where adenine appears on one chain, thymine appears on the other, and wherever guanine appears on one chain, cytosine appears on the other. The obvious implication of this feature is that for DNA molecules isolated from any source whatever, the molar amount of adenine is equal to that for thymine ($A = T$), and the molar amount of guanine is equal to that for cytosine ($G = C$). (There is no feature of the model that restricts the relative amounts of AT pairs to GC pairs. In fact, the instructions in each set of genic material are coded by the sequences of the four nucleotides.) Chemical analysis for the base constitution of DNA molecules has provided excellent evidence in favor of the two equalities $A = T$ and $G = C$.

An experiment from the laboratory of Arthur Kornberg adds another type of confirmation to the Watson–Crick model. Enzymes occur in nature that can hydrolytically cleave the phosphate-sugar ester bonds of DNA backbones. One of these enzymes cleaves only the bond connecting the number 5 carbon of each sugar to phosphate. If hydrolysis is permitted to proceed to completion, the DNA molecules in a treated solution are all cleaved to nucleotides. (Hydrogen bonds between bases are not strong enough to keep the two members of a single bonded pair together throughout the steps of the procedure.) These nucleotides differ from those shown in Fig. 3.4 in that each phosphate group is attached to the number 3 carbon of the sugar rather than to the number 5 carbon. This enzymatic tool makes it possible to determine the frequency with which the four nucleotides occur as nearest neighbors to each other along the chains of DNA molecules. The experimental analysis follows.

Adenine nucleotide (for instance) labeled with radioactive phosphorus (P^{32}) in the phosphate group attached to the number 5 carbon of the sugar is "fed" to a system (see Chapter 4) that is synthesizing DNA. DNA is then isolated from the system and enzymatically cleaved at the number 5 carbon atoms. The nucleotides are next isolated and separated into the four kinds. The amount of radioactivity in each type of nucleotide is determined. The radioactivity shown by a given type of nucleotide must be proportional to the frequency with which that nucleotide occurs bonded by the phosphate group running from its sugar-carbon atom 3 to the 5 carbon in the sugar of an adenine nucleotide. The experiment is repeated by feeding each of the other radioactive nucleotides, hydrolyzing, and measuring radioactivities of the isolated nucleotides. The data considered collectively provide an estimate of the frequency with which each of the nearest neighbor associations shown at the top of the following page occurs. (P is phosphate.)

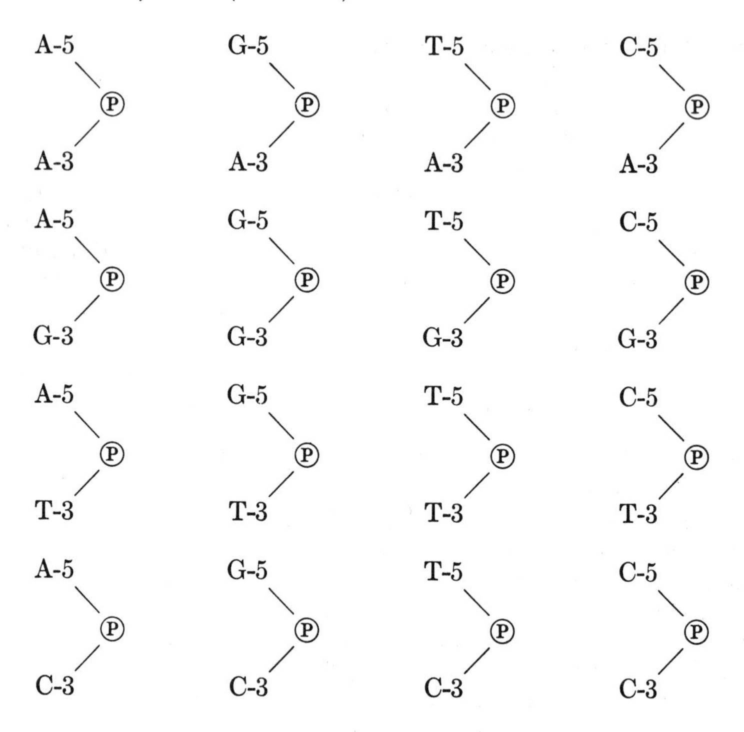

To understand the outcome of these experiments we must refer to the diagram of a DNA chain in Fig. 3.5. Note that a DNA chain has polarity; on one end of the chain the terminal nucleotide is attached to the chain at the number 3 carbon atom of its sugar, while the terminal nucleotide at the other end is attached by its number 5 carbon atom. If we look now at Fig. 3.7, we see that in a DNA molecule, the two chains run in opposite directions. This feature of the model makes special predictions about the relative frequencies of nearest neighbor associations. Some of the relations to be expected are evident from an examination of Fig. 3.7; e.g.,

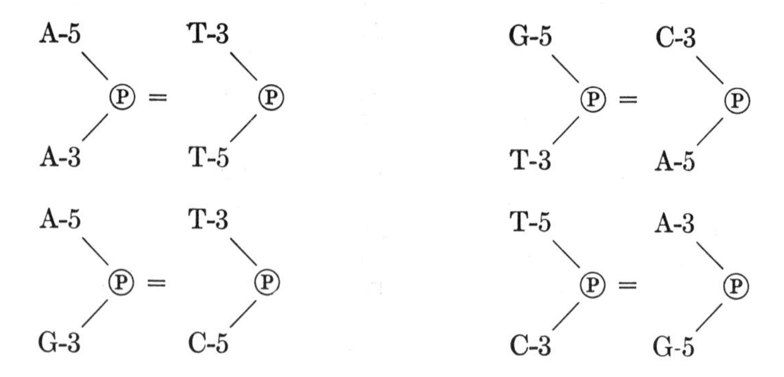

You may deduce other relations for yourself. The outcome of the experiments was in excellent accord with the predicted relationships.

The opening paragraph of this chapter qualified the statement that DNA occurs in nature as a pair of chains. Some very small bacteriophages contain only single DNA chains. After the DNA from these phages invades a bacterial cell, however, it becomes double chained like other DNA. This behavior points up one feature of DNA implied previously in this chapter. Since DNA is genic material, it must contain in some fashion the information for ordering the amino acids in proteins and otherwise directing the life cycle of each cell. As pointed out by Watson and Crick, the only reasonable source for such specificity is in the sequence in which the nucleotides occur within a DNA molecule. (We shall see ample verification for this surmise in Chapter 5 and in later chapters.) The sequence of nucleotides on one chain of a DNA molecule has point-to-point complementarity with the sequence on the other chain. The two chains, then, carry exactly the same information. The little phages containing single DNA chains seem merely to have reduced the genic baggage that they must carry in their quest for a host cell.

The rare deoxyribonucleotides

The opening paragraph of this chapter hedged also with respect to the nucleotide composition of DNA. Although cytosine, thymine, adenine, and guanine are the four most common bases, several others do occur in various DNA's. Each of these rarer bases substitutes for one of the common bases. Thus, for instance, phage T2 contains no cytosine but instead contains 5-hydroxymethyl cytosine. The amount of this latter base in T2 is equal to the amount of guanine. It is apparent, therefore, that in T2 5-hydroxymethyl cytosine plays the role that cytosine plays in other creatures. The DNA of a number of organisms contains both cytosine and methyl cytosine. In these cases, the sum of the amounts of these two bases is equal to the amount of guanine. A virus has been discovered that contains 5-hydroxymethyl uracil in place of thymine. The purine 6-methylamino purine occurs in some DNA in low frequency in place of adenine. The structural formulas of these rare bases are shown and compared with their common analogues in Fig. 3.9 on the following page.

The structure of viral RNA

RNA (*r*ibo*n*ucleic *a*cid) is cataloged by biologists according to the function it performs. In Hartman and Suskind's *Gene Action* in this series, three kinds of RNA that play key roles in the biosynthesis of

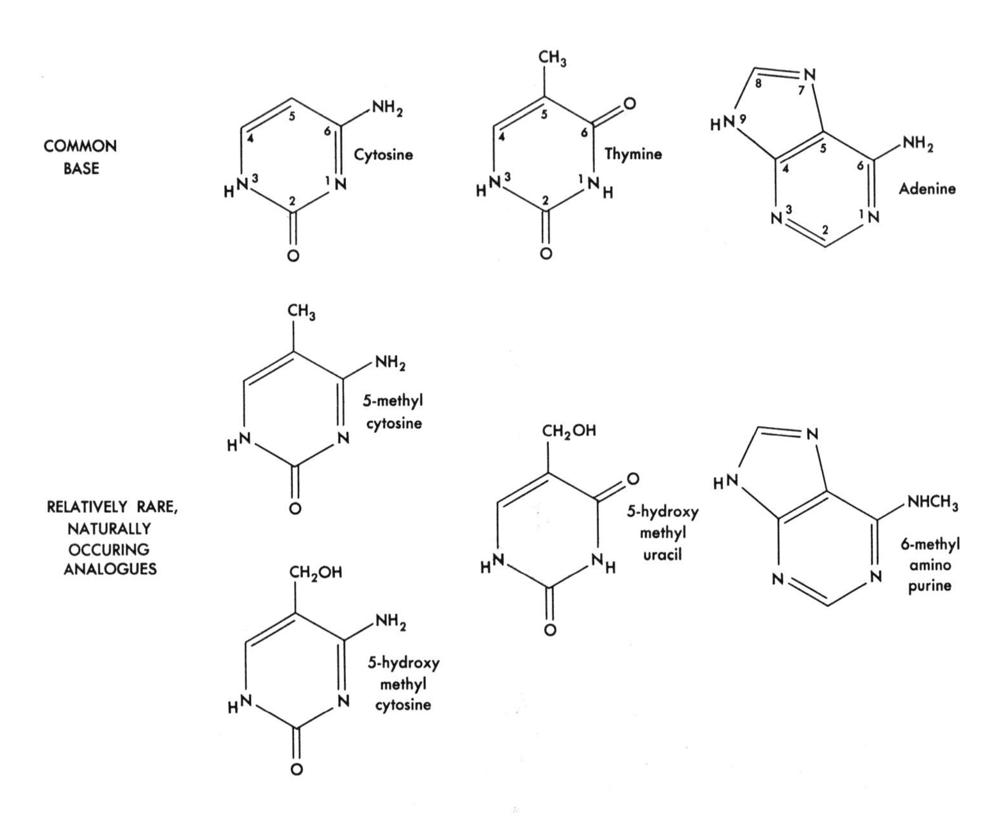

Fig. 3.9. The structures of relatively rare nitrogenous bases that are known to occur in DNA from some sources. The structural formulas of the rare bases are compared with the formulas of the common bases for which they substitute. Note that the substitutions on the unusual bases avoid those positions involved in the adenine–thymine and guanine–cytosine hydrogen bonding (cf. Fig. 3.6).

proteins will be examined. We shall focus our attention here on RNA that plays a genetic role, i.e., on "viral RNA."

In all RNA the constituents are ribose (a 5-carbon sugar), phosphoric acid, and (usually) four nitrogenous bases. Although in some of the RNA's involved in protein synthesis a number of kinds of bases occur in small amounts in addition to the four predominant ones, in viral RNA only the bases adenine, guanine, cytosine, and uracil occur. Uracil is a pyrimidine identical to thymine except that the 5-position is not methylated.

The constituents of RNA are bonded together much as are the constituents of DNA. RNA is a long polymer with a sugar-phosphate backbone. The phosphate bridge connects the number 5 carbon atom of one ribose to the number 3 carbon atom of the next. The bases are attached to the ribose in exactly the same way the bases in DNA are attached to the deoxyribose. A stretch of an RNA chain is diagrammed in Fig. 3.10.

The RNA in the mature particles of most RNA-containing viruses is single-chained. Probably this RNA becomes double-chained during the duplicative stage of the virus life cycle.

The chain length of viral RNA is of the order of 10^3 to 10^4 nucleotides, depending on the virus from which it is isolated.

Fig. 3.10. A stretch of an RNA (*ribonucleic acid*) chain. Each of its four bases is attached to a "backbone" of ribose units connected by 3′–5′ phosphate "bridges." The base sequence has been chosen willy-nilly.

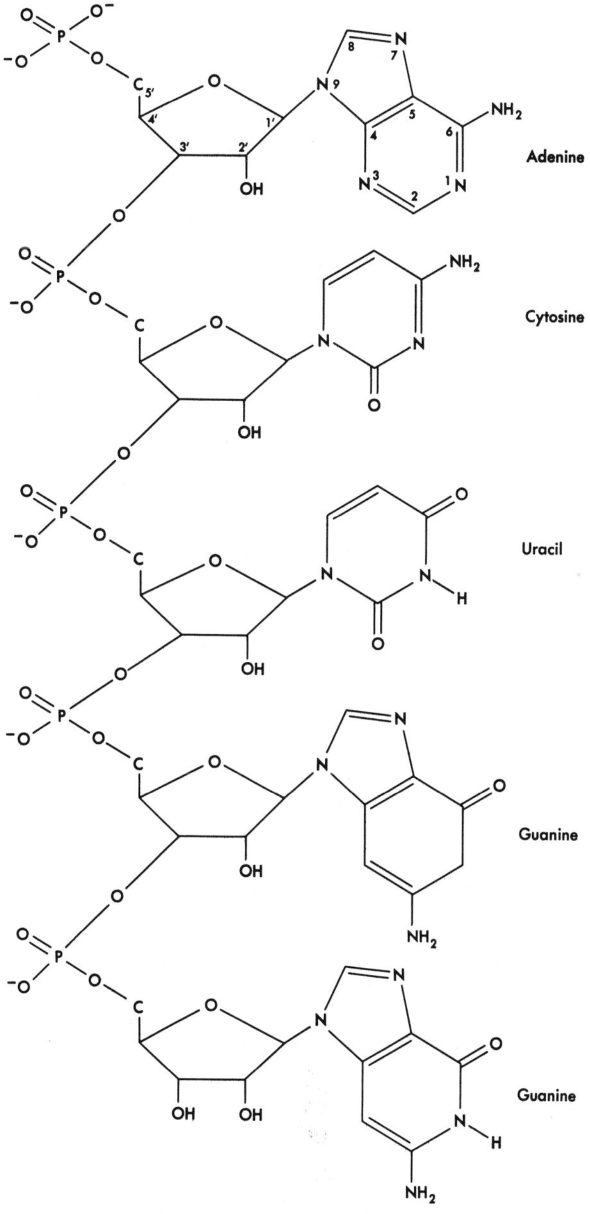

Summary

Perhaps you should reread this chapter. The next two chapters describe behavior of DNA in terms of its structure. Subsequent chapters will discuss genetic phenomena at some remove from the molecular level; in these chapters we shall share the aims of today's geneticist—to seek explanations for these phenomena in terms of the structure and properties of DNA.

References

Watson, James D., and Francis H. C. Crick, "Molecular Structure of Nucleic Acids: A Structure for Deoxyribose Nucleic Acid," *Nature, 171* (1953), 737-38. Reprinted in *Classic Papers in Genetics,* J. A. Peters, ed. (Englewood Cliffs, N.J.: Prentice-Hall, Inc., 1959), pp. 241-43. The announcement of the Watson–Crick model for the structure of DNA.

Wilkins, Maurice, "Physical Studies of the Molecular Structure of Deoxyribose Nucleic Acid and Nucleoprotein," *Cold Spring Harbor Symp. Quant. Biol., 21* (1956), 75-90. Continued study following the Watson–Crick announcement served to substantiate their model while refining some of the dimensional parameters.

Problems

3.1. Calculate the molecular weights of (a) cytosine, (b) thymine, (c) guanine, (d) adenine. Calculate the molecular weights of the corresponding nucleosides: (e) deoxycytidine, (f) (deoxy)thymidine, (g) deoxyguanosine, (h) deoxyadenosine. Calculate the approximate molecular weight of (i) the sodium salt of a DNA molecule containing 10^4 base pairs in which the two possible base pairs are assumed to be about equally frequent.

3.2. The phage T2 contains not more than 2×10^5 nucleotide pairs. How long is the total DNA complement of T2? (The head of T2 is roughly a sphere of diameter 800Å. *E. coli* is a cylinder about 2 μ long and 0.5 μ in diameter.)

3.3. How many twists (approximately) are in a DNA molecule whose molecular weight is 10^8?

3.4. At any level in a DNA molecule there may exist any one of four possible base-pair configurations:

adenine–thymine (AT)	guanine–cytosine (GC)
thymine–adenine (TA)	cytosine–guanine (CG)

Calculate the number of possible sequences that can conceivably exist in a DNA molecule 10^4 nucleotide pairs long (with no restriction on the relative frequencies of the four kinds of base pairs).

Duplication of DNA

It was once a favorite hunch in biology that genetic specificity might be transmitted to proteins as the contours of a mold are transferred to the statue made in it; i.e., it was imagined that the genic material could direct the synthesis of compounds structurally complementary to itself. Such a notion is appealing both to naïve intuition and to the principles of structural chemistry. However, the idea is a bit demanding biologically; it insists that genic material can conduct the synthesis of both complementary molecules (genic products) and identical molecules (new genic material). Perhaps it was partly because of such considerations that the self-complementarity of the DNA molecule suggested to Watson and Crick the mode of duplication of DNA.

Crick and Watson hypothesized that prior to (or during) duplication the two chains of a DNA molecule separate. Each chain then directs the synthesis of a chain complementary to itself. It is usually imagined that synthesis of a new chain starts at one end of an old chain and proceeds step by step to the other end. The manner in which the polymerization is initiated is not easily visualized, but, once started, the rules for its continuation seem simple. The growing end of a new chain and the not-yet-copied portion of the old chain form a "corner." The corner formed at any particular level can be comfortably occupied by only one of the four nucleotides. Only that nucleotide will be incorporated that can simul-

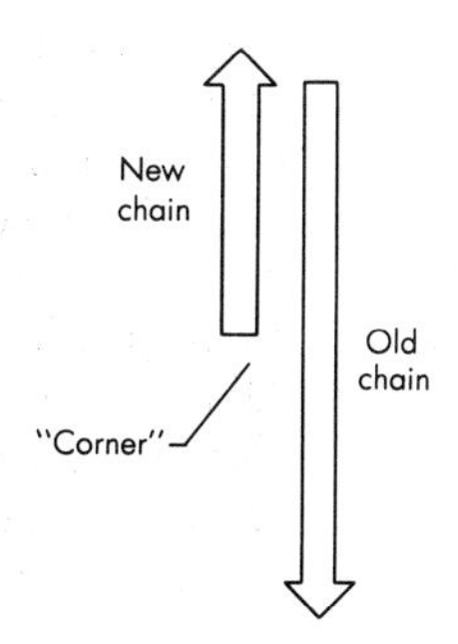

taneously hydrogen bond with the old chain *and* present its phosphate group at the proper position to be bonded to the growing end of the new chain. In a later section of this chapter we shall look at the mechanism of the bonding of each nucleotide to the growing end of a new chain.

"Semiconservative transmission" of isotopic label

A feature of the Watson–Crick hypothesis for DNA duplication is that half of each molecule ends up in a daughter molecule as a consequence of duplication; i.e., duplication is "semiconservative." (This is not an essential feature of the self-complementary aspect of the Watson–Crick hypothesis, but it certainly seems like the simplest prediction. At the expense of complicating our view of nature we might suppose that following duplication the four DNA chains are assorted into the two daughter molecules by a superimposed rule assuring that the two old chains wind up together in one molecule and the two new chains in the other. Such a "conservative" duplication scheme, still utilizing the self-complementary feature of the Watson–Crick hypothesis, has been used for explaining some genetic experiments and some physical observations. However, at the moment there is no direct evidence that "conservative" duplication can occur.) The prediction of semiconservative duplication implicit in the Watson–Crick hypothesis was confirmed by the outcome of an experiment performed by M. S. Meselson and myself in the late 1950's (see Fig. 4.1). We grew bacteria (*Escherichia coli*) for many generations in a simple medium in which the only nitrogen source was NH_4Cl. The ammonium chloride contained only the heavy isotope of nitrogen, N^{15}. A preponderance of the ordinary isotope of nitrogen, N^{14}, was then added to the medium. At intervals cells were removed, and the DNA was extracted from them. The density of the individual molecules in each sample was then examined by the method of equilibrium density gradient centrifugation to determine the relative content of N^{15} and N^{14}.

In the equilibrium density gradient method a concentrated salt solution (e.g., CsCl in water) containing the DNA to be examined is centrifuged in an analytical ultracentrifuge. The CsCl, since it is more dense than water, tends to sediment to the outside of the cell. This tendency to sediment is opposed by diffusion, however, and after about eight hours (under the conditions employed) the concentration distribution of CsCl in the cell is essentially stable. The resulting smooth concentration gradient results in a density gradient. The DNA molecules in the cell are driven to the region in the gradient that corresponds to their own effective density. The bands into which the DNA collects are of finite width, since DNA, too, is subject to diffusion. By the end of about twenty hours the sedimentation and diffusion forces acting on the DNA are essentially in equilibrium, and the concentration of DNA can be photographically determined. The principal

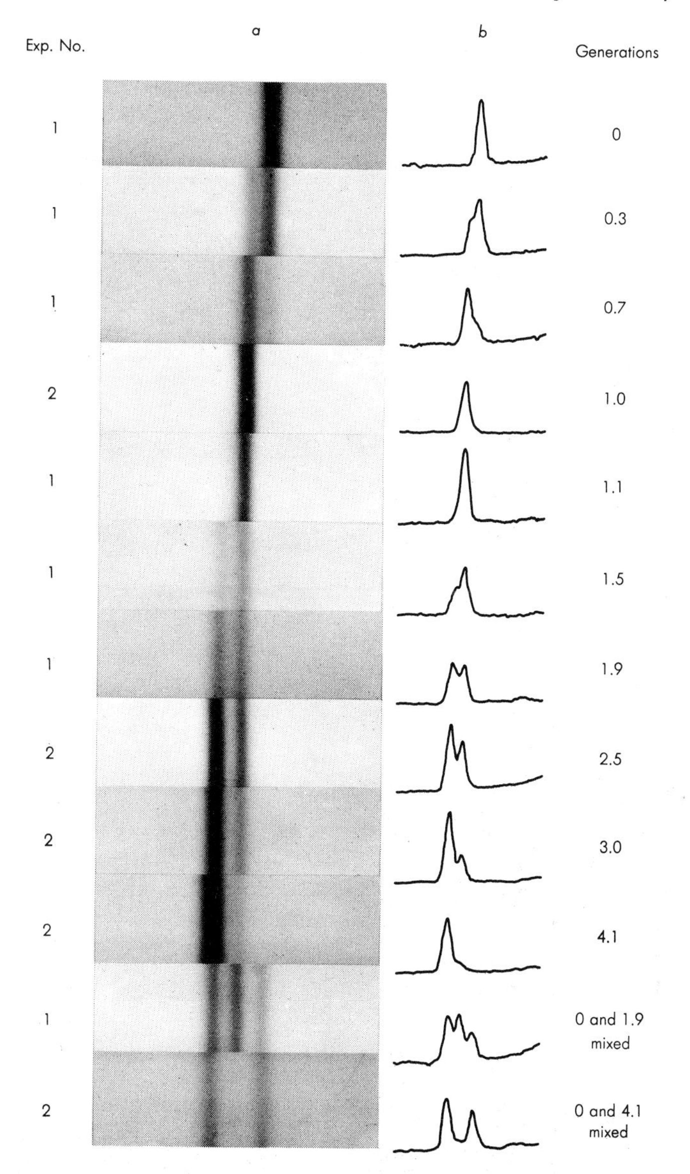

Fig. 4.1. (*a*) Ultraviolet absorption photographs showing DNA bands resulting from density gradient centrifugation of lysates of bacteria sampled at various times after the addition of an excess of N^{14} substrates to a growing N^{15}-labeled culture. The density of the CsCl solution increases to the right. Regions of equal density occupy the same horizontal position on each photograph. (*b*) Microdensitometer tracings of the DNA bands shown in the adjacent photographs. The microdensitometer pen displacement above the base line is directly proportional to the concentration of DNA. The degree of labeling of a species of DNA corresponds to the relative position of its bands between the bands of fully labeled and unlabeled DNA in the lowermost frame, which serves as a density reference. This figure, reproduced with permission of M. S. Meselson, appeared in *Proc. Nat. Acad. Sci. U.S., 44* (1958), 675.

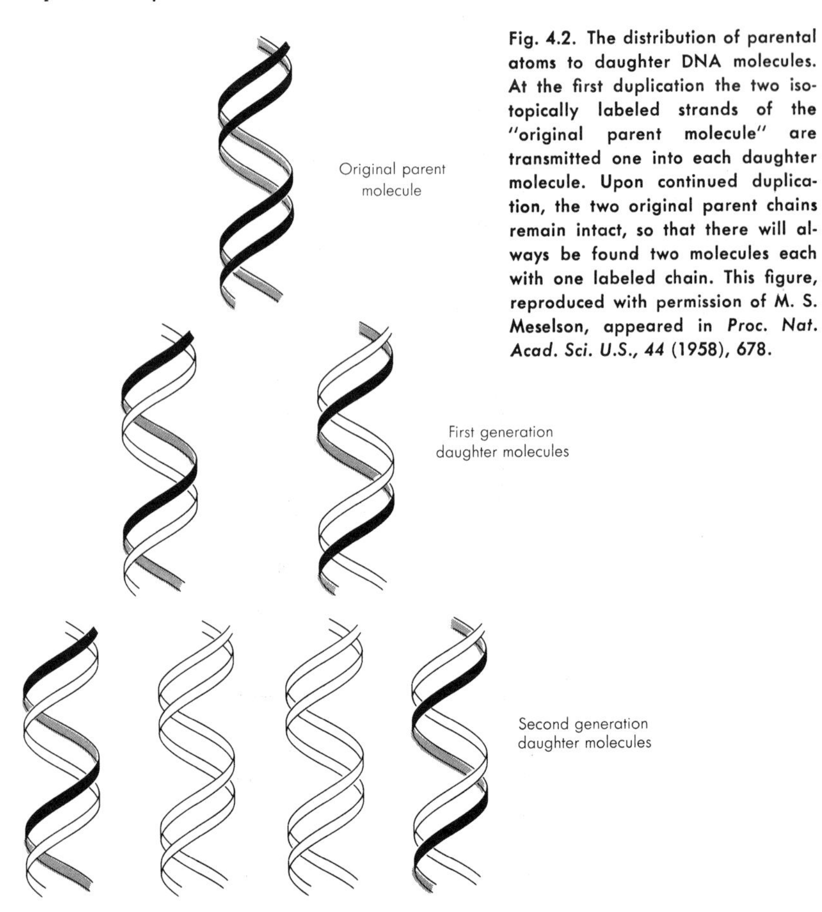

Fig. 4.2. The distribution of parental atoms to daughter DNA molecules. At the first duplication the two isotopically labeled strands of the "original parent molecule" are transmitted one into each daughter molecule. Upon continued duplication, the two original parent chains remain intact, so that there will always be found two molecules each with one labeled chain. This figure, reproduced with permission of M. S. Meselson, appeared in *Proc. Nat. Acad. Sci. U.S.*, *44* (1958), 678.

result of the experiment was that after one doubling of the *E. coli* population each molecule contained equal amounts of N^{15} and N^{14}. After two doublings, there were present equal numbers of such "half-labeled" molecules and completely N^{14}-containing molecules (see Fig. 4.1). The results of this experiment, interpreted in terms of the Watson–Crick hypothesis for DNA duplication, are schematically summarized in Fig. 4.2.

It is clear from the foregoing that the net result of DNA duplication is that two separated old chains each are found associated with their complementary new chains. The sequence of steps by which this is brought about, however, is not specified by the above considerations. The intuition of many who speculated on this sequence was that chain synthesis went on hand in hand with chain separation. A molecule in the act of duplication would, therefore, look like that in Fig. 4.3. John Cairns provided strong experimental support for this idea in the 1960's. Cairns used autoradiography (see the legend to Fig. 6.3) to

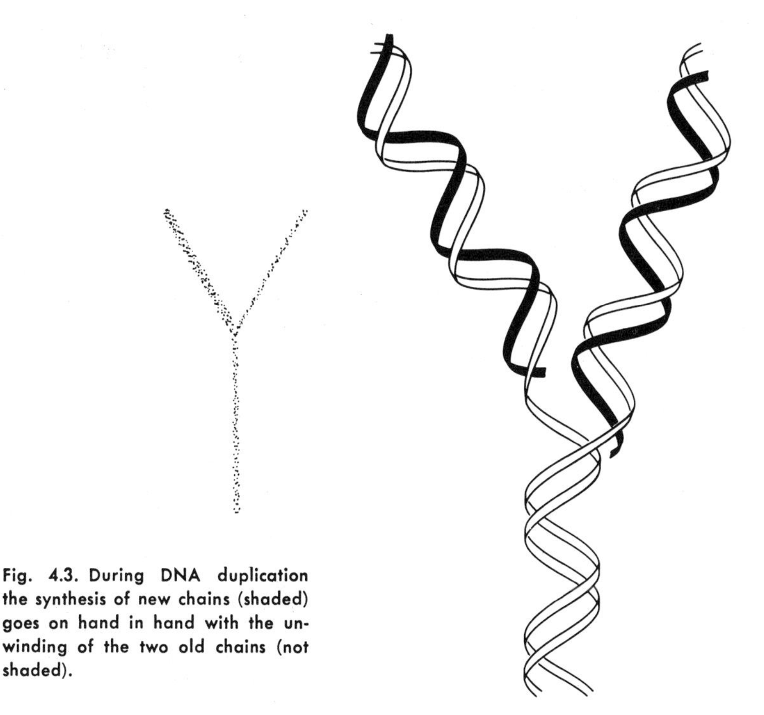

Fig. 4.3. During DNA duplication the synthesis of new chains (shaded) goes on hand in hand with the unwinding of the two old chains (not shaded).

examine the DNA from *E. coli* that had been allowed to duplicate for varying periods of time in radioactive thymidine. In molecules that were undergoing their second round of duplication in radioactive medium, a region could be seen that gave an autoradiographic image like that shown in the small drawing to the left of Fig. 4.3. Under the experimental conditions employed, the density of ion tracks in the image is proportional to the number of labeled chains at any level in the molecule. Convince yourself that the pattern above would result if the half-labeled molecules arising as a result of one generation in labeled medium were undergoing their second duplication in labeled medium in the fashion diagrammed in Fig. 4.3.

In vitro synthesis of DNA

Considerable detail regarding the mechanism of DNA synthesis has been provided by the studies of Arthur Kornberg and his collaborators. They have isolated (from bacteria) an enzyme that can catalyze the polymerization of nucleoside triphosphates in the presence of DNA. The newly synthesized DNA chains have the same relative frequencies of the four bases as do the chains of the "primer" DNA. This in vitro system probably reflects to some extent the steps in the in vivo synthesis of DNA. (The experiment on nearest neighbor frequencies described in Chapter 3 was carried out in vitro with this DNA-synthesizing system.) The steps in DNA synthesis identified or implied by studies of this system are diagrammed in Fig. 4.4.

Duplication of single-chained genic material

We have encountered viruses that in their infectious stage contain single-chained nucleic acid, either DNA or RNA. Experimental observations on their duplication are compatible with the prejudices you probably share with me by now. It seems likely that single-chain nucleic acid directs the enzymatic synthesis of a chain

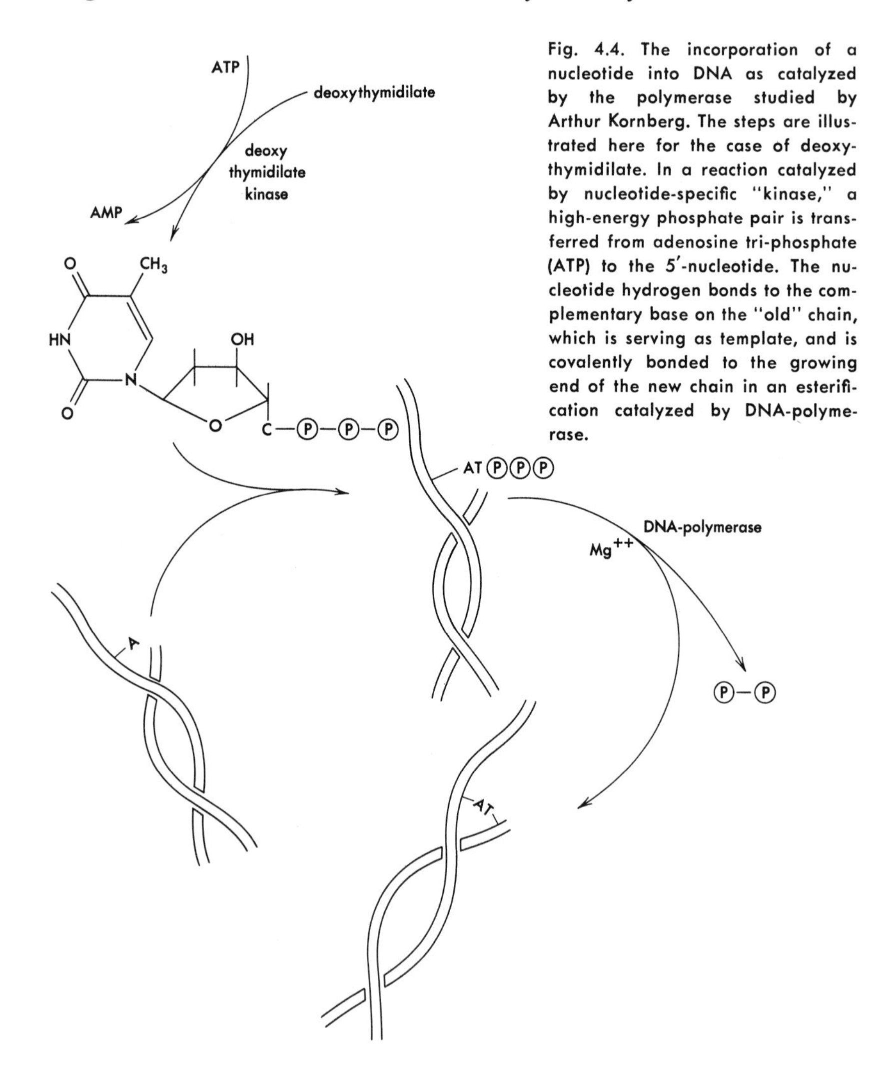

Fig. 4.4. The incorporation of a nucleotide into DNA as catalyzed by the polymerase studied by Arthur Kornberg. The steps are illustrated here for the case of deoxythymidilate. In a reaction catalyzed by nucleotide-specific "kinase," a high-energy phosphate pair is transferred from adenosine tri-phosphate (ATP) to the 5′-nucleotide. The nucleotide hydrogen bonds to the complementary base on the "old" chain, which is serving as template, and is covalently bonded to the growing end of the new chain in an esterification catalyzed by DNA-polymerase.

complementary to itself. Subsequently, the nucleic acid duplicates as does "ordinary" double-chained nucleic acid. At some step prior to, or concomitant with, encapsulation of the nucleic acid in the protein coat of the mature progeny virus particles, the complementary chains of the replicating form dissociate. Only one type of chain ends up in mature particles.

It appears very likely that the picture presented describes the mode of duplication of single-chained DNA of viral origin; application of the scheme to RNA viruses is more speculative.

Summary

The outlines of the mechanism of DNA duplication were correctly drawn from a knowledge of the structure of the molecule. A property of genic material as basic as duplication is mutation. In the next chapter we shall see that a mechanism of mutation was also correctly proposed by the inventors of the Watson–Crick DNA model.

References

Cairns, John, "The Bacterial Chromosome and Its Manner of Replication as Seen by Autoradiography," *J. Mol. Biol.*, *6* (1963), 208-13. The replication of DNA really *does* go hand in hand with chain separation.

Kornberg, Arthur, "The Biologic Synthesis of Deoxyribonucleic Acid," Nobel Lecture, 1959. Reprinted in *Genetics,* I. H. Herskowitz (Boston: Little, Brown & Co., 1962), pp. S-50–S-64. A review of the prize-winning work of the author and his colleagues on the biochemistry of DNA synthesis.

Meselson, M. S., and F. W. Stahl, "The Replication of DNA in *Escherichia coli,*" *Proc. Nat. Acad. Sci. U.S.*, *44* (1958), 671-82. Duplication of DNA is shown to be semiconservative, as predicted by Watson and Crick.

Problems

4.1. Consider a DNA molecule in which every nitrogen atom is "labeled," i.e., in which every nitrogen atom is the heavy isotope (N^{15}) instead of the normal isotope (N^{14}). Imagine that such a molecule is permitted to duplicate in an environment in which all of the nitrogen is N^{14}.

(a) After one duplication, how many of the (two) molecules present contain some N^{15}?

(b) After three duplications, how many of the (eight) molecules present contain some N^{15}?

(c) Suppose that, after two duplications, the (four) molecules are returned to an environment containing only N^{15}. After one duplication in the N^{15} environment, how many of the (eight) molecules will contain some N^{14}?

(d) If each of the molecules in Problem 4.1a were cut transversely (as one cuts a piece of string) into a number of pieces, how many of the resulting pieces would contain some N^{15}? (This experiment has been done using ultrasonic vibrations to cut the DNA. I trust you deduced the same answer that was found experimentally.)

4.2. Nowadays, one laboratory uses N^{15} and C^{13} simultaneously in "DNA-transfer" experiments. What do you calculate is the approximate density difference between "heavy" and "light" DNA in this case? (Assume equal frequencies of adenine and guanine.)

4.3. Following infection of *E. coli* by a single particle of the phage T2, there is no DNA synthesis for 6 minutes. Duplication of phage DNA then begins and proceeds exponentially until about 30 (say 32) phage equivalents of DNA are present in the cell. At this time mature nonmultiplying particles begin to appear, their number increasing linearly with time. DNA synthesis continues at a constant rate equal to the rate of maturation so that the amount of "naked" DNA remains constant. The exponential phase of DNA duplication, which begins 6 minutes after infection, lasts until about 11 minutes after infection.

(a) What is the "generation time" for the T2 DNA during the exponential phase of duplication? (In Chapter 6 we shall examine the evidence which suggests that the DNA of a T2 phage particle is one large molecule about 2×10^5 nucleotide pairs long.)

(b) What is the rate of synthesis of T2 DNA in units of nucleotide pairs/minute?

Five

Mutation of DNA

The hypothesis for the mechanism of DNA duplication discussed in Chapter 4 was suggested to Watson and Crick by the molecular structure of DNA. The duplication scheme in turn suggested to its authors a mechanism of mutation.

Tautomerism of bases

Each of the four bases in DNA can exist in states alternative to those shown in the previous figures. The transitions to these rare states occur by rearrangements (tautomeric shifts) in the distribution of electrons and protons in the molecule. The (interesting) tautomeric alternatives for each of the four bases are shown in Fig. 5.1. When a base is in its rare state, it cannot form a hydrogen-bonded pair within a DNA molecule with its usual partner. A purine in its rare state can, however, form a fine pair with the "wrong" pyrimidine, and a pyrimidine in its rare state can form a fine pair with the "wrong" purine. The four pairings that can occur when one member (but not both) of a base pair has undergone a tautomeric shift are diagrammed in Fig. 5.2.

Watson and Crick suggested that the occurrence of the rare tautomeric alternatives for each of the bases provides a mechanism for mutation during DNA duplication. If a base in an old chain is in its rare form at the moment that the growing end of the complementary new

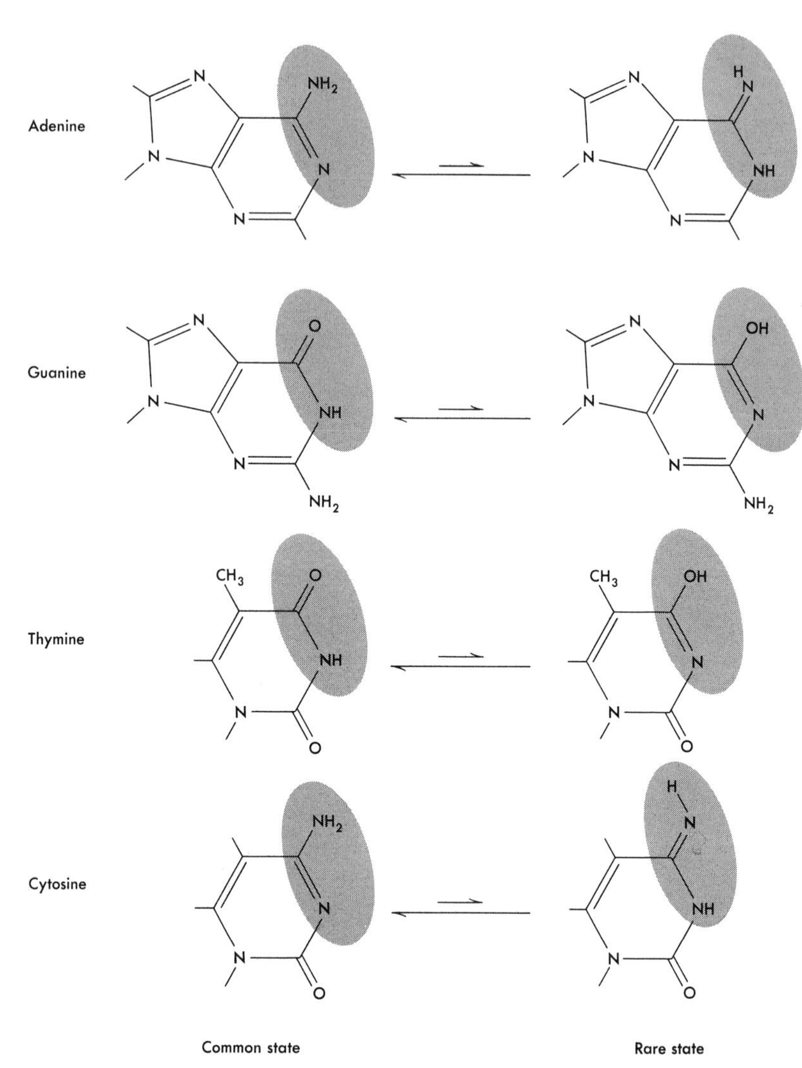

Fig. 5.1. Tautomerism of the bases of DNA. Structural formulas for each of the four bases of DNA can be written in several alternative ways. The alternatives differ from each other only by rearrangements of protons and electrons. These rearrangements are symbolized in the structural formulas by changes in the positions of H atoms and of double bonds. Any rearrangement involving only protons and electrons may be written as long as the valences of the constituent atoms are respected. The frequencies of occurrence of each of the tautomers can sometimes be determined by physicochemical studies. The bases of DNA occur overwhelmingly in the states shown on the left. The tautomer suspected to be important in the origin of mutations is shown on the right.

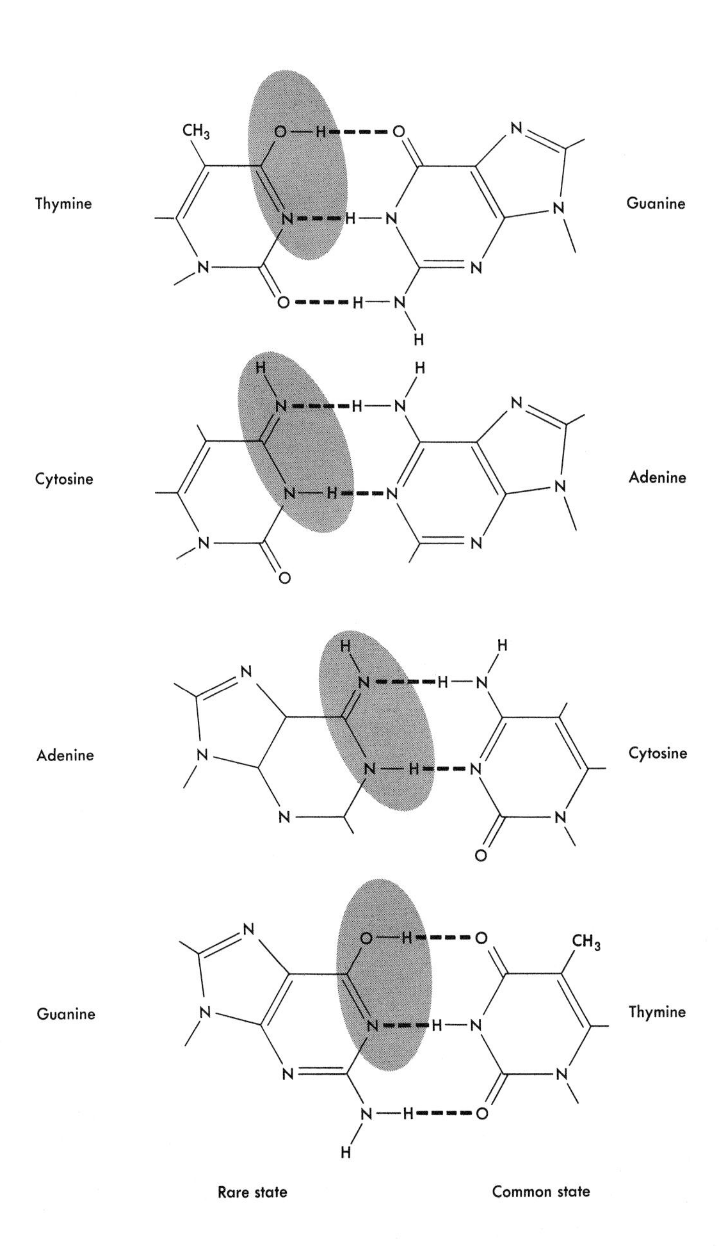

Fig. 5.2. "Forbidden base pairs" resulting from tautomerization. The specific hydrogen-bonding properties of each of the bases are reversed by the tautomeric shifts in Fig. 5.1.

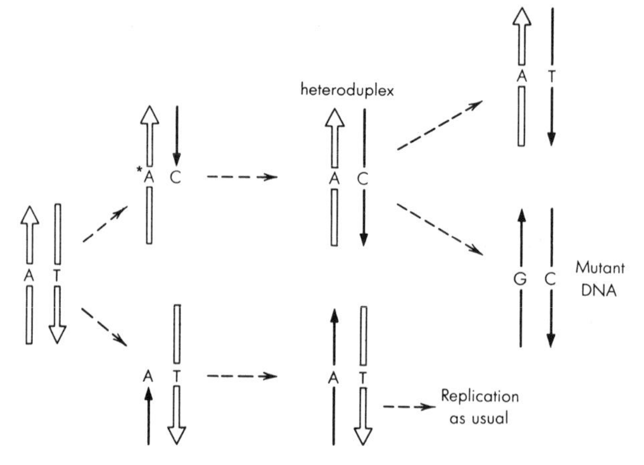

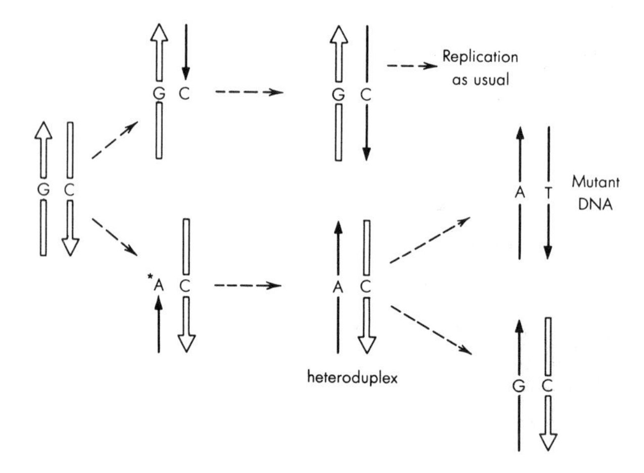

Fig. 5.3. The consequences of tautomerization of an adenine residue at the time of DNA duplication. Tautomerization can be instrumental in the induction of base-pair transitions in two ways. (1) A base, adenine in the case depicted here, already in a DNA chain may tautomerize at the moment a new DNA chain is being synthesized along it. (2) Adenine deoxyribose triphosphate about to be incorporated at the growing end of a new chain may tautomerize. Note that these two cases have opposite results. The former case induces the transition AT to GC while the latter induces the transition GC to AT. Note also that for each case the first product of the mistake is a heteroduplex, which at the next duplication gives rise to a molecule of the original type as well as to a mutated molecule.

chain reaches it, a wrong nucleotide can be added to the growing end. Similarly, if the base of a nucleoside triphosphate is in *its* rare form, it may be added to the growing end of a new chain at an incorrect level in a duplicating molecule. In either case, the primary consequence of this mistake is the formation of a DNA molecule that contains a "forbidden" base pair. Such a heteroduplex gives rise upon duplication to two kinds of DNA molecules. One is identical to the original DNA; the other has undergone a base-pair transition at the level of the pairing mistake induced by the tautomeric shift. (In keeping with the custom of the day, *transition* will be used to denote only the changes AT $\rightleftharpoons$ GC and their obvious equivalents TA $\rightleftharpoons$ CG. The other possible base-pair changes are summarized by the following scheme:

$$\begin{array}{ccc} AT & \rightleftharpoons & CG \\ \upharpoonleft\downharpoonright & & \upharpoonleft\downharpoonright \\ TA & \rightleftharpoons & GC \end{array}$$

These changes are referred to collectively as transversions.) The steps in transition by tautomerism are outlined in Fig. 5.3.

It has been suggested that transitions can also arise as a consequence of ionization of a base at the time of DNA duplication. The loss of the proton from the number 1 nitrogen of either thymine or guanine permits the formation of a TG base pair. The base-pairing configurations that become permissible because of these ionizations are diagrammed in Fig. 5.4.

Mutation by base-pair transitions

The notion of mutagenesis as a result of base-pairing mistakes at the time of DNA duplication has received considerable experimental support. Much of the support has come from studies of *rII* mutants of the *coli* phage T4. The discussion that follows is not meant to create the impression that mutation is fully understood, or even that what understanding we have rests primarily on studies of the *rII* system; but the clarity of concept and the simple consistency of results that have characterized many of the experiments and most of the publications dealing with *rII* make it useful for illustration.

T4*rII* particles differ from T4r^+ (wild-type) particles in two useful respects. An appreciation of the usefulness of this experimental material requires short digressions into technic and history.

Technic. Phage particles are conveniently enumerated by distributing a measured volume of a phage suspension upon the surface of a solid nutrient-agar medium along with about 100 million host bacterial cells. This is accomplished by suspending the phages and cells

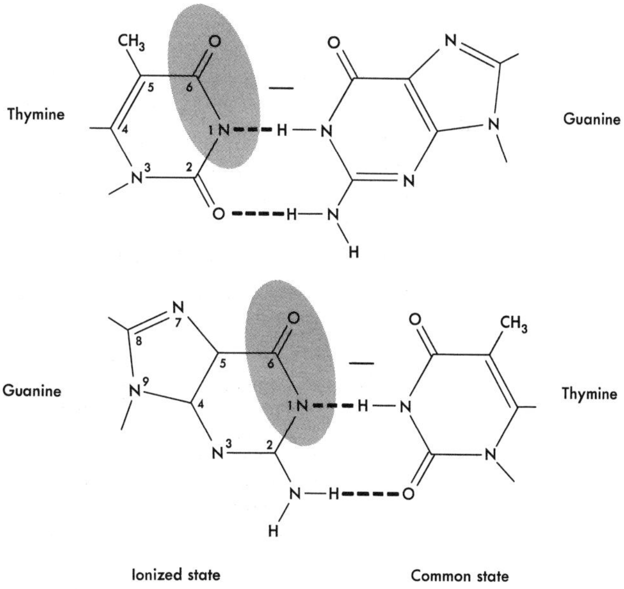

Fig. 5.4. "Forbidden base pairs" resulting from ionization of the number 1 nitrogen. The loss of the proton from the number 1 nitrogen of thymine or guanine permits the formation of the base pair TG. The double bond from the number 6 carbons to the oxygens could as well be drawn between the 6 and 1 positions of the rings.

Ionized state

Common state

in a few ml. of melted nutrient agar and then pouring the inoculated agar onto the surface of the solid agar medium. The melted agar spreads across the surface and then, within a few minutes, hardens to a semisolid consistency. The bacterial cells multiply to form an array of colonies so dense as to constitute a uniform sheet of bacterial cells in the top agar layer. Each of the phage particles adsorbs to, multiplies within, and lyses a nearby bacterial cell. Upon their release, the progeny particles adsorb to neighboring cells and repeat the cycle. Within a few hours a number of holes (plaques) corresponding to the number of particles introduced into the top layer agar have been eaten in the otherwise continuous sheet of bacterial cells.

T4*rII* particles, when grown with *E. coli* strain B, make plaques that are larger and have a sharper edge than do those of T4r^+. When grown with *E. coli* K12(λ),[1] T4r^+ particles make plaques as they do on strain B; T4*rII* particles, however, fail to make plaques on K12(λ).

History I. S. E. Luria showed that mutation rates in bacteriophages can be determined by application of the same equations used to measure mutation rates in bacterial cultures (see Chapter 1). An implication of Eqs. 1.1 and 1.3 is that the number of mutations occurring in the last generation of a bacterial culture is equal to the sum of the number occurring in all the generations previous to that one. These same equations imply that the generation during which a mutation occurs can be determined by the number of (mutant) offspring deriving from the mutational event. A mutation in the *i*th generation gives rise to twice as many mutants in a culture as one occurring in the *i*th + 1 generation; a mutation in the last generation leaves but one (mutant) offspring.

Luria examined the phage progeny liberated by individual bacteria infected by r^+ phages. The average phage yield per cell was about eighty particles. Of those cells that yielded some *r* particles, half yielded only one *r* particle; the other half yielded two or more. Similarly, a quarter of the bursting cells yielded four or more mutant particles and an eighth yielded eight or more, etc. This observation clearly implies that phages multiply "exponentially" (as do bacteria) and justifies the use of the same definition for mutation rate in phages as is used for bacteria.[2]

History II. Seymour Benzer recognized the virtues of the T4*rII* mutants and set an extraordinary example of vigorous exploitation.

[1] *E. coli* strain K12 carrying the prophage λ (see Chapter 9).

[2] This discussion is a simplification. The two step nature of the production of a mutant DNA molecule diagrammed in Fig. 5.3 is not incorporated in the algebra; neither is the multinucleate nature of many bacteria—a situation that can lead to analogous analytical ambiguities. For phages the situation is even more complicated (see Problem 4.3). Nevertheless, the growth equation (Eq. 1.1) and the definition of mutation rate (Eq. 1.3) are useful approximations.

Thousands of *rII* mutations have been isolated from independent occurrences of mutation. Most of these mutants are distinguishable from each other by one or both of two criteria. (1) Their rates of back mutation to r^+ may be distinguishable. (2) When grown *together* in a host cell they may produce r^+ progeny in a higher frequency than when either strain is grown by itself. (This observation, without further explanation, serves to establish the nonidentity of the two mutant strains. The nature of the interaction that leads to the production of r^+ progeny is described in Chapters 7 and 8.) Those of the *rII* mutants that arise *à la* Watson and Crick must be supposed to represent transitions of single base pairs. Furthermore, the ability to distinguish most of the mutants from each other indicates that alterations of each of a large number of base pairs can be studied. In Chapter 8 we shall examine the evidence that each of these alterations influencing the *rII* phenotype occurs within a restricted region of the T4 DNA. At this point it is the uniqueness of many of the *rII* mutations that is important. This uniqueness coupled with the (re)discovery of chemical mutagenesis in viruses made possible an experimental challenge of the Watson–Crick hypothesis for the mechanism of mutation.

Base-pair transitions induced by 5-bromouracil and nitrous acid

5-bromouracil (5BU) is a structural analogue of thymine (5-methyl uracil). When phages are grown in the presence of 5BU, they may incorporate it into their newly synthesized chains of DNA. Indeed, if the infected cells are prevented from making thymine, all of the positions normally occupied by thymine in the newly synthesized chains are instead occupied by 5BU. Phages grown under conditions that permit 5BU incorporation have a higher than normal mutation rate. "To be expected," say the philosophical heirs of Watson and Crick. "From what we know of the effects of bromine substitution in cyclic organic compounds we shouldn't be surprised if the rate of tautomerism to its rare (enol) state should be higher than that for thymine." On somewhat more solid theoretical grounds they predict also that the frequency of ionization of the number 1 ring nitrogen of 5BU should be higher than that for thymine. The experimental chemical evidence up to late 1962 favors the latter view. Figure 5.5 shows the tautomeric forms and the ionized forms of thymine and its analogue 5BU respectively. An inspection of Fig. 5.5 reveals that tautomerization and ionization have a structural consequence in common; they both involve the loss of hydrogen from the number 1 nitrogen. This common structural feature has evoked the common proposals regarding their roles in mutagenesis. It appears that most 5BU-induced mutagenesis is caused by ionization.

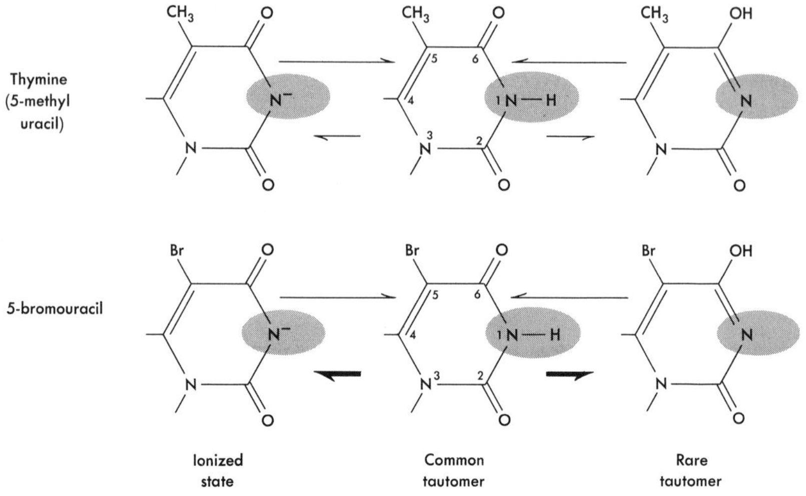

Thymine (5-methyl uracil)

5-bromouracil

Ionized state — Common tautomer — Rare tautomer

Fig. 5.5. The molecular basis of mutation induction by 5-bromouracil. 5BU is structurally so similar to thymine that it can substitute for thymine in the biosynthesis of DNA. A consequence of this substitution is a high mutation rate. The greater degree of ionization, and perhaps of tautomerization, of 5BU probably accounts for its mutagenic properties. The two proposed mechanisms have in common the loss of hydrogen from the number 1 ring position.

The notion that 5BU induces mutations by inducing base-pair transitions is strengthened by several observations. We can discuss two of these now.

(1) Mutations induced in phages by duplication in the presence of 5BU can be induced to back mutate (revert) under the same conditions. This observation is easily understood if 5BU can induce both GC-to-AT and AT-to-GC transitions as described in Fig. 5.3 for spontaneous mutations arising from tautomerism of adenine.

(2) Among 5BU-induced mutants, some can revert only when 5BU is present as a precursor in DNA synthesis; others can revert when the only 5BU present is that already incorporated in DNA in place of thymine. Presumably the latter class represents transitions of the type

$$\underset{\text{mutant}}{\text{AT}} \xrightarrow{\text{5BU in DNA}} \underset{\text{wild type}}{\text{GC}}$$

while the former class is of the other type:

$$\underset{\text{mutant}}{\text{GC}} \xrightarrow{\text{5BU precursor}} \underset{\text{wild type}}{\text{AT}}$$

Nitrous acid (HNO_2) treatment of -NH_2 substituted purines and pyrimidines results in replacement of the -NH_2 (amino) group by an -OH (hydroxyl) group. The consequences of HNO_2 treatment of

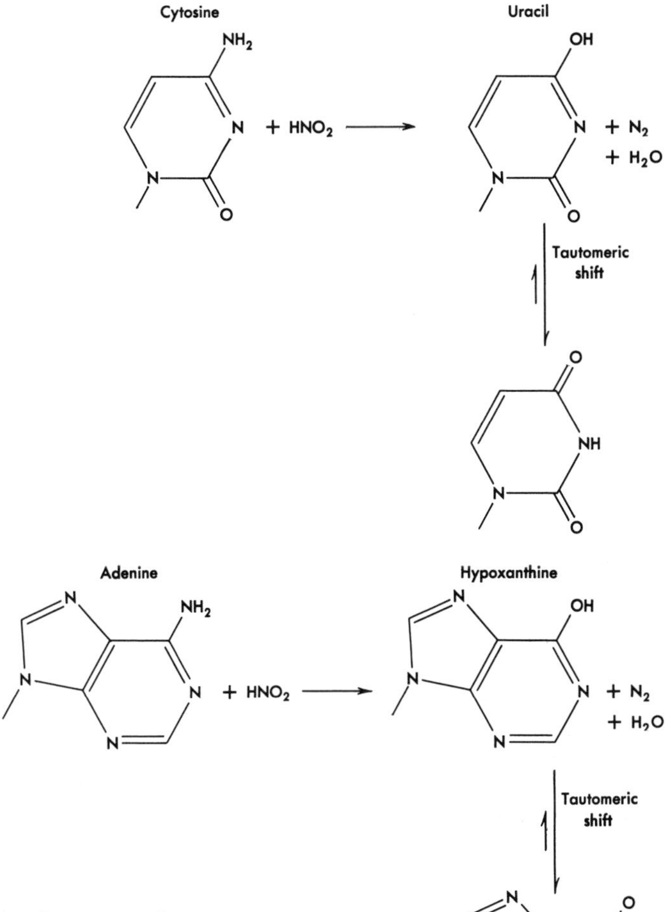

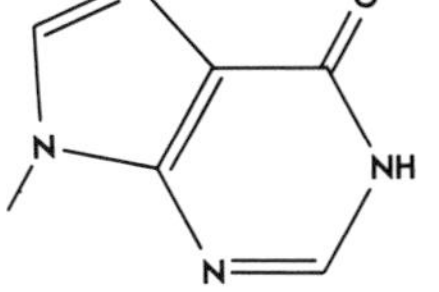

Fig. 5.6. Deamination by nitrous acid (HNO_2). The final products of the deamination of cytosine and adenine are bases that have the hydrogen-bonding specificities of thymine and guanine respectively.

adenine and cytosine are diagrammed in Fig. 5.6. The deamination of cytosine leads to the formation of a product (uracil) whose hydrogen-bonding properties are essentially those of thymine; the deamination of adenine results in the formation of hypoxanthine, whose hydrogen-bonding properties are similar to those of guanine. There are two reasons for thinking that the deamination of guanine is not mutagenic. (1) Xanthine, the product of deamination of guanine, has hydrogen-bonding properties like those of guanine, rather than like those of adenine. (2) Xanthine deoxyribose triphospate is not a substrate for the in vitro DNA-synthesizing system of Kornberg. The failure of the synthesizing system to recognize xanthine as a precursor of DNA synthesis suggests that it may also balk at recognizing xanthine as a bona fide component of the template.

The treatment of phage (or other) DNA by HNO_2 results in the deamination of amino-substituted bases. When HNO_2-treated T4r^+ are permitted to infect cells and multiply, a few per cent of the particles give rise to *r* offspring. Almost all of these few per cent *also* give rise to r^+ offspring. This result is in fine agreement with our pictures of the nature of HNO_2 mutagenesis and of a semiconservative mode of DNA duplication.

According to our picture, nitrous acid treatment of DNA can result in the transitions AT to GC and GC to AT. A prediction of this notion is that HNO_2-induced *rII* mutants should be revertible with HNO_2. And so they are.

A joint consideration of our pictures of 5BU mutagenesis and HNO_2 mutagenesis leads to the prediction that these mutagens should be capable of reverting each other's induced mutants. Indeed they do. The picture is further strengthened by the reported detection of heteroduplex particles as the first products of mutagenesis by 5BU.

The reader might be able to spot a number of other predictions of the notion that 5BU and HNO_2 induce base-pair transitions. Some of these predictions have been tested; others await testing.

Other mutations in DNA

The mechanism of mutation proposed by Watson and Crick (as somewhat modified later) is the induction of base-pair transitions as a consequence of tautomerism or ionization. The validity of this hypothesis in accounting for at least *some* mutational events is substantiated by the experimental studies with HNO_2 and 5BU among others. It is clear, however, that not all mutations within DNA molecules occur by this mechanism. Some of the evidence for the existence of other kinds of mutation comes from studies of experimentally induced reverse mutation of *rII* mutants. As discussed above, transition mutations "should" be revertible by 5BU, HNO_2, or other agents that induce transitions. In keeping with this notion it was recorded that 5BU and HNO_2 *do* generally revert their own and each other's induced mutants. Agents are known, however, that produce mutations most of which are not revertible by transition-inducing agents. Furthermore, among "spontaneous" *rII* mutants only about 15 per cent can be induced to revert with transition-inducing mutagens. The nature of some of these other classes of DNA mutations and speculations as to their mode of origin are discussed below. A particularly straightforward demonstration of a "deletion" will be discussed first.

In the phage λ several mutations resulting from the loss of stretches of the DNA molecule have been characterized. These spontaneous mutants were originally detected by the perturbations they introduce in the growth cycle of this phage. One result of these perturbations is altered plaque morphology. The density of these mutant phage particles has been examined by CsCl density-gradient centrifugation and found to be less than that of wild-type λ. This reduced density of the whole particle suggests that the ratio of DNA (density in CsCl = 1.7 gm./cc.) to protein (density in CsCl = 1.3 gm./cc.) is less in these mutants than in wild-type λ. If it is assumed that this change in ratio is a result solely of a reduction in the amount of DNA, it can be calculated for one of these mutants that 15 per cent of the nucleotide pairs are missing. The validity of this estimate is verifiable by independent methods. Direct chemical analysis might well work, but, in fact, a somewhat easier method was employed.

Phage particles containing large amounts of radioactive phosphorus (P^{32}) in their DNA are measurably unstable; they are rendered incapable of forming plaques (they "suicide") as a result of the disintegration of the incorporated P^{32}. Decay of a P^{32} atom results in rupture at the level of the decay of the DNA chain in which that atom was incorporated. With a probability of about 0.1, a decay leads to the nearby simultaneous scission of the other chain of the DNA molecule. Such a double chain scission results in inactivation of the particle. The rate at which a population of P^{32}-labeled particles commits suicide depends on the rate at which lethal decays occur within the particle; this in turn depends on the number of P^{32} atoms in the particles. For two populations containing the same ratio of P^{32} to total phosphorus atoms, the one with particles containing the larger amount of DNA will contain the larger number of P^{32} atoms and will, consequently, suicide faster. Wild-type λ and the λ mutant with the density reduction corresponding to a 15 per cent reduction in DNA content were grown to give the same extent of labeling per P atom; the mutant was observed to suicide 15 per cent slower than wild type. Since wild-type λ contains about 70,000 nucleotide pairs, the mutant appears to be missing about 10,000 nucleotide pairs. Seldom are mutations that are known to be within the limits of a single DNA molecule sufficiently gross to submit to such straightforward characterization. Mutations to *rII* resulting from deletions of smaller stretches of DNA in the *rII* region of T4 have been well studied, however. A description of the method of analysis of these deletions is best deferred until Chapter 8, but the nature of some of the conclusions may be indicated here.

Deletions occur ranging in size from one nucleotide pair up to as much as or more than two thousand nucleotide pairs. Only the very smallest of the deletions revert to wild type at a measurable rate (mutation rate greater than about 10^{-9}). The usual failure of deletions to revert is easily understood; gross changes in the nucleotide sequence of a DNA molecule are not likely to be repaired by the chance process of mutation.

The rate of appearance of small deletions or additions can be experimentally increased. In Hartman and Suskind's *Gene Action* in this series, evidence is introduced indicating that the class of organic compounds called acridines induces deletions or additions, or both, of single base pairs or of a few base pairs. Acridines are mutagenic to phages only when applied to the intracellular phase of the life cycle. Nitrous acid, on the other hand, can induce deletions of variable size as a result of treating the mature phage particles. In contrast to the case for transition induction, the mechanism of deletion induction by HNO_2 is not known.

It seems likely that base-pair transversions do occur, but direct support for their existence was lacking in late 1962.

Summary

Two kinds of mutations (heritable alterations) have been shown to occur within the limits of single DNA molecules—base-pair transitions and deletions. It is likely that transversions and additions can occur as well.

Genetic systems of higher order of complexity than a single DNA molecule are known to undergo other kinds of mutation. A comprehensive discussion of such mutations can be found in Carl P. Swanson's *Cytogenetics,* a volume in this series.

References

Kreig, David R., "Specificity of Chemical Mutagenesis," *Progress in Nucleic Acid Research, 2* (1963), 125-168. Rarely has so much been said so well in so few words.

Luria, S. E., "The Frequency Distribution of Spontaneous Bacteriophage Mutants as Evidence for the Exponential Rate of Phage Reproduction, *Cold Spring Harbor Symp. Quant. Biol., 16* (1951), 463-70. Reprinted in *Papers on Bacterial Viruses,* G. S. Stent, ed. (Boston: Little, Brown & Co., 1960), pp. 139-50. Viruses became organisms as a consequence of Luria's presentation—mutationally speaking, they get and beget like the rest of us.

Terzaghi, B. E., George Streisinger, and F. W. Stahl, "The Mechanism of 5-Bromouracil Mutagenesis in the Bacteriophage T4," *Proc. Nat. Acad. Sci. U.S., 48* (1962), 1519-24. Some 5BU-revertible mutations in phage T4 can revert only when 5BU is present in the intracellular environment of the multiplying phage; others can revert when 5BU-substituted particles are permitted to duplicate in an ordinary intracellular environment.

Watson, James D., and Francis H. C. Crick, "The Structure of DNA," *Cold Spring Harbor Symp. Quant. Biol., 18* (1953), 123-31. Reprinted in *Papers on Bacterial Viruses,* pp. 193-208. A discussion of the evidence underlying the Watson–Crick formulation for the structure of DNA and their hypothesis for the mechanisms of duplication and mutation that derive from it.

Problems

5.1. Some bacteria were infected with exactly one each of wild-type T4. The yields from many individual cells ("single bursts") were then examined for mutations to the r genotype. The total yield from each cell was about 200. Of 10,000 single bursts examined, 200 had at least one r mutant. What is the mutation rate to r?

5.2. Donald MacDonald Green and David Krieg treated T4 with ethyl methane sulfonate (EMS). They then removed the EMS and infected some bacteria with the treated phages. They diluted the infected cells before lysis into many tubes such that each tube got far less than 1 cell infected with a viable phage. After lysis, they plated the contents of the tubes on an indicator strain on which r plaques look different from wild-type T4 plaques and counted the number of r plaques. They observed:

Clone size	*Number of clones*
1	38
2-3	21
4-7	12
8-15	22
16-31	23
32-63	20
64-127	17
128-255	6
256	1

In what way do these data differ from those of Luria? What do you conclude?

5.3. (a) Phage particles treated with nitrous acid lose their ability to form plaques; with increasing dose, a decreasing fraction of the particles make plaques. The following sort of data can be obtained:

Duration of treatment with constant HNO_2 *concentration*	*Fraction of phage surviving*
0 min.	1
1	0.1
2	0.01
3	0.001

(1) How many deaminations must occur to kill a particle?

(2) After two mintes' treatment, what fraction of the particles have incurred exactly 3 lethal deaminations?

(b) Examination of the survivors of HNO_2 treatment reveals that the frequency of mutants among survivors is increased with increasing dose. Data for the rate of reverse mutation of any particular rII marker are easily obtained by plating an HNO_2-treated rII stock on *E. coli* K(λ), on which only $r+$ and $r+/rII$ heteroduplex phages make plaques. The primary measurement made is (live $r+$ and $r+/rII$) per ml. Suppose 10^9 phage per ml. were treated under the same conditions used in Problem 5.3a, and the following data were obtained:

Duration of treatment	(*Live* r^+ *and* r^+/rII) *per ml.*
0 min.	10
0.05	460
0.1	810
0.5	1,600
1	1,000
2	200
3	30

Assume that killing and mutagenesis are independent events.

(1) How many deaminations are required to make a phage that will plate on K(λ)?

(2) What fraction of the live phages are induced to revert per minute of treatment?

(c) At any dose, what is the ratio of reversions at the marker studied to all lethal deaminations?

5.4. Particles of a strain of phage suspected of "carrying" a genic deletion were grown along with wild-type λ in an environment heavily laced with P^{32}. The P^{32}-labeled offspring particles were collected and the titers of viable particles of each type were determined at intervals. Suppose the following data were obtained:

Fraction of P^{32} *decayed*	*Titer of wild type*	*Titer of deletion mutant*
0	1.0×10^9	1.0×10^9
0.2	9.5×10^7	1.2×10^8
0.4	9.0×10^6	1.5×10^7
0.6	8.5×10^5	1.7×10^6

What fraction of the wild-type DNA is missing in the deletion mutant?

Organization of DNA

The purpose of this chapter is threefold: (1) to examine the spatial organization of DNA within a creature, (2) to examine the way in which DNA organization is modified in time as a creature proceeds through its life cycle, and (3) to make these examinations for creatures of various degrees of biological complexity. We can recognize three levels of complexity without making any particular effort to justify the selection beyond the recognition of their heuristic convenience.

The first level includes the viruses. We may characterize the creatures of this level as those that can multiply only *within* cells because of their own lack of essential energy-providing and synthetic metabolic processes. They have nucleic acid associated (in some cases) at some stages in their life cycle with protein that aids in their dissemination.

At the second level are those creatures that *can* lead relatively independent existences (some are even photosynthetic!) but that lack important structural features characteristic of the cells of creatures in level III. Another name for the creatures in level II is bacteria.

In level III are all those creatures composed of various and varying numbers of cells each of which has a nucleus clearly differentiated from a cytoplasm. All, or nearly all, of the DNA of such creatures resides in the nuclei of their cells where it is organized into Chromosomes.[1] For convenience, the creatures in the three levels will be called viruses, bacteria, and higher organisms respectively.

Packing of DNA

Creatures at all levels face a common intriguing problem relative to the organization of their DNA. For each of them, there is a stage (or there are stages) in the life cycle when the DNA is very tightly packed into a small space. Our notions about DNA organization must take this property of genic structures into account while admitting that its basis is not understood.

We may illustrate the "packing problem" by considering the dimensions of a mature, infectious T4 particle and of the DNA packed within it.

The T4 DNA has a total volume that we can calculate using the dimensional parameters for DNA given in Fig. 3.8 in conjunction with the chemically determined nucleotide content of a T4 particle of 2×10^5 nucleotide pairs. We may approximate the shape of a DNA molecule as a cylinder. Then:

$$\begin{array}{c}\text{Volume of} \\ \text{T4 DNA}\end{array} = \begin{array}{c}\text{Cross sectional} \\ \text{area of DNA}\end{array} \times \text{Total length of T4 DNA}$$

$$= \pi(10^{-7}\text{ cm.})^2 \quad \times \left(\frac{3.4 \times 10^{-8}\text{ cm.}}{\text{nuc. pair}}\right)(2 \times 10^5\text{ nuc. pairs})$$

$$= 2 \times 10^{-16}\text{ cm.}^3$$

The volume into which this DNA is packed can be estimated from electron micrographs of mature phage particles like the one in Fig. 6.1. With the aid of the scale given in that figure you can calculate this volume. The figure (not including the tail) is a bipyramidal hexagonical pyramid. An outer layer of protein of about 50Å thickness surrounds the DNA; lateral dimensions taken from the figure should be appropriately reduced to be applicable to the DNA. Using the micrograph in Fig. 6.1, I calculated 2×10^{-16} cm.^{3} as the volume into which the phage DNA is packed.

The nature of the packing problem is more dramatically illustrated by a comparison of the *length* of the phage DNA with the *diameter* of the phage head. If we approximate the morphology of the phage head by a hollow sphere of comparable internal volume, it would have an inside diameter of a bit less than 800Å. This dimension is about 1,000 times smaller than the total length of the DNA in T4 (see Fig. 6.2a).

[1] *Chromosome* with a capital *C* will be used to refer to the genic structures of higher organisms; the word was originally coined in their behalf. It is capitalized out of respect and also to distinguish it from *chromosome* with a lower case *c*, which will refer to the genic structure of *any* creature.

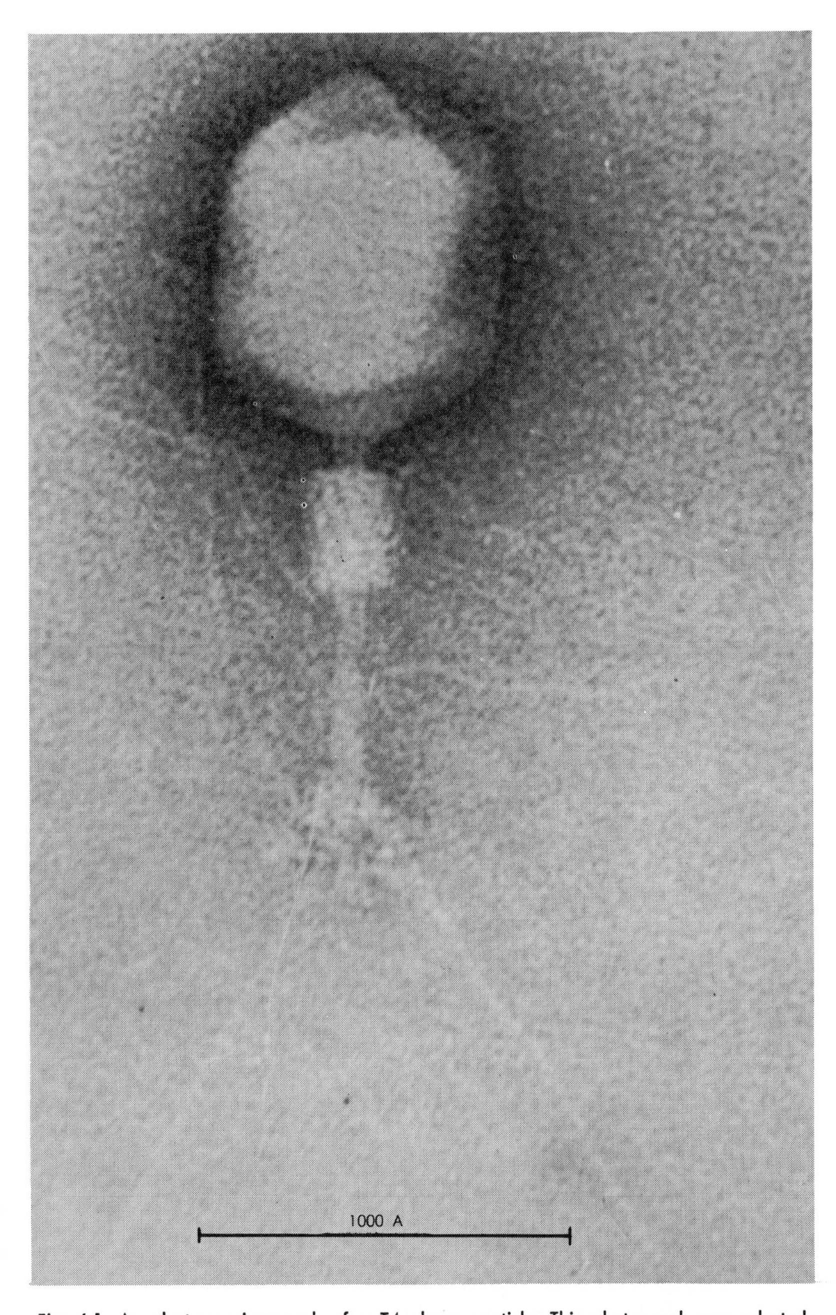

Fig. 6.1. An electron micrograph of a T4 phage particle. This photograph was selected because the method by which it was prepared (phosphotungstic acid embedding of the specimen) accurately preserves the dimensions of the specimen. The appearance of the tail of the particle is abnormal for reasons that do not interest us now. The volume into which the DNA is packed within the 50-Å-thick protein "skull" can be estimated from this figure to be 2×10^{-16} cm^3. This number is about equal to the volume of the DNA of this phage calculated from the Watson–Crick dimensional parameters for DNA. This photograph, kindly supplied by R. W. Horne, appeared in *J. Mol. Biol.*, *1* (1959), 281.

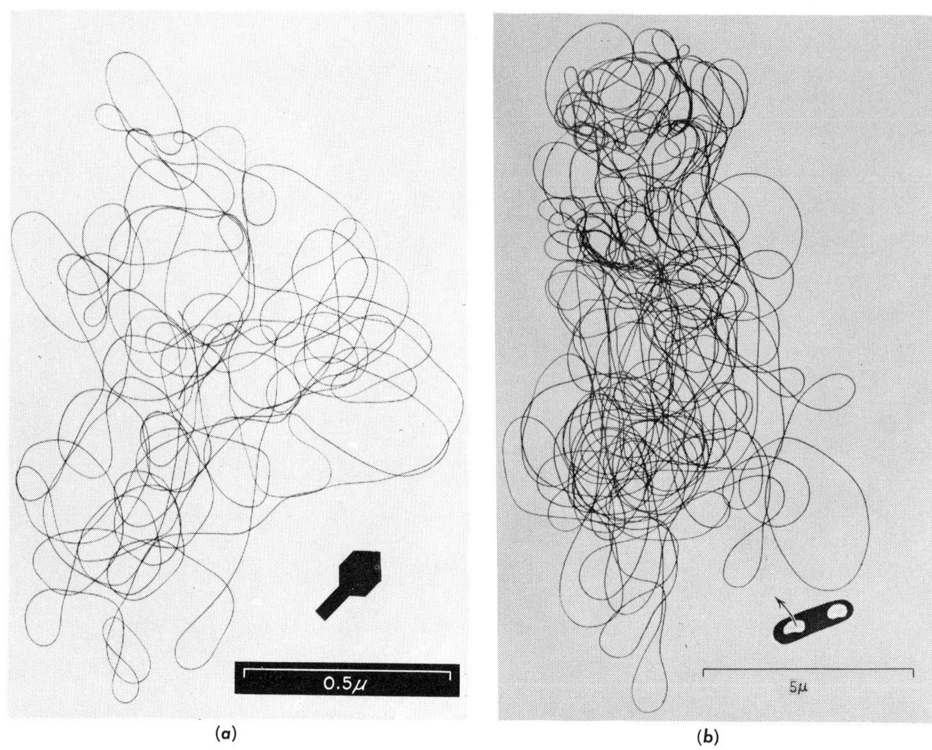

Fig. 6.2. The total length of the DNA of a virus, a bacterium, and a higher organism compared to scale with the structures into which the DNA is organized. The three parts of the figure are not to the same scale. (*a*) Bacteriophage T4. The chromosome of T4 is about 60μ long. (*b*) Bacterium *E. coli*. The chromosome of *E. coli* is about 1,000μ long (1 mm.). (c) *Drosophila melanogaster,* a "higher organism." The total DNA complement of a cell of a fruit fly is about 16 mm. long. The figure depicts the Chromosomes as they appear in mitotic metaphase (see page 74) in a cell containing two complete sets of Chromosomes (a *diploid* cell).

As indicated previously, the packing problem is not unique to viruses. In Figs. 6.2b and 6.2c the total length of DNA in one genome (one complete set of genic material) for bacteria and for the fruit fly *Drosophila* are compared to scale with the structures into which that DNA is packed at some stages of the life cycles of the respective cell types.

The phage chromosome

When phages are gently disrupted, the entire DNA content of each particle can be isolated as part of a single structure (the chromosome of the phage). This structure is long and thin; electron microscopic observation indicates that it has the width (20Å) of a single DNA molecule. Autoradiography (see Fig. 6.3) reveals that it has the length ($\sim 60\,\mu$) for T2 or T4 equal to the total length of the DNA in a phage particle. There seems to be no compelling reason to think that this structure is other than a *single* DNA molecule depending for its primary structural integrity only on bonds accounted for by the Watson–Crick DNA model. (We include in the category of "Watson–Crick bonds" the ionic bonds between the phosphate groups of the DNA and the cations that neutralize them.) Our inability to make a statement stronger than this is partly a consequence of the embryonic state of this area of investigation. Perhaps more importantly, however, it reflects the extreme difficulty of *ruling out* the existence of substances whose presence may be biologically critical but the amount of which is very small relative to the amount of DNA in the chromosome. Should small amounts of substances other than DNA be identified as being intimately associated with the isolated phage chromosomes, the nature of their association may prove even more difficult to demonstrate. This problem will plague us throughout this chapter. The temptation to dismiss it is tempered by the feeling that some kind of "joints" in the DNA may be required to account for the precise folding of the molecule that apparently accompanies condensation.

A second uncertainty with respect to the structure of a phage chromosome or any other chromosome follows from our present inability to get a clear answer to the question "Is the phosphate-sugar backbone of the two complementary DNA chains continuous throughout the entire length of the chromosome, or even throughout the entire length of the one or more individual DNA molecules?" We may give substance to this question by considering a hypothetical chromosome, containing only DNA, for which the sugar-phosphate backbones are *not* continuous:

or

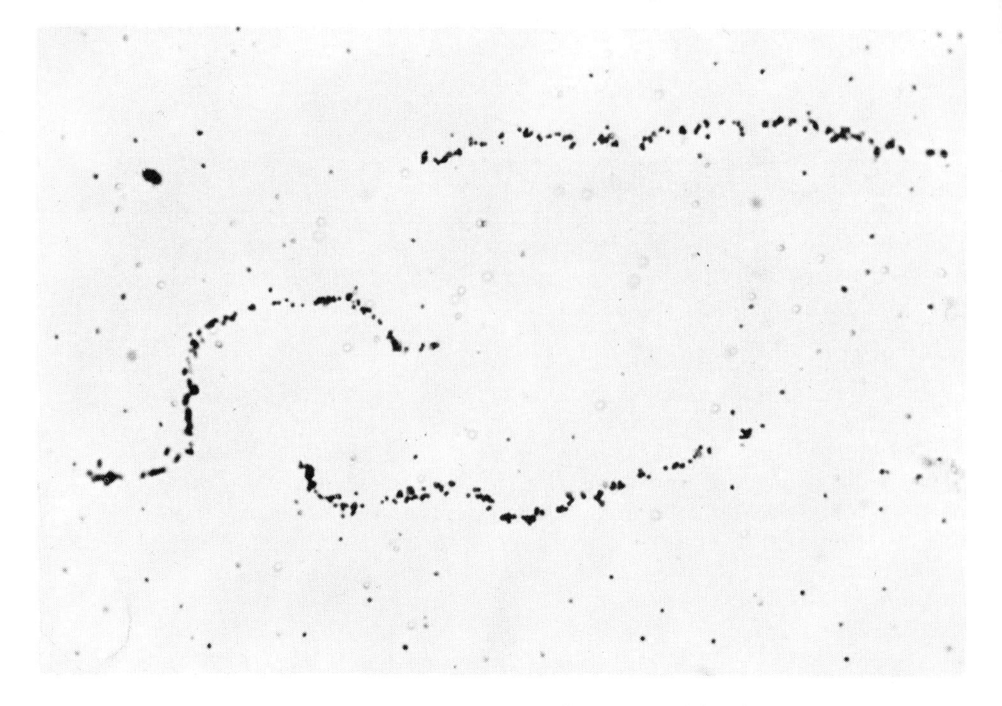

Fig. 6.3. Autoradiographic images of isolated chromosomes of the phage T4. Bacteria growing in medium containing tritium (H^3)-labeled thymidine were infected by phages. The progeny phages emerging were isolated and gently disrupted. The disrupted particles were suspended in melted photographic emulsion that was then gently poured onto a smooth glass plate. When the emulsion had hardened, the plates were stored until an appreciable number of H^3 atoms in each chromosome had decayed. The electrons ejected from the nucleus of a decaying H^3 atom travel but a short distance through the emulsion sensitizing a small number of silver grains. Upon development of the emulsion, the sensitized grains appear as very short "tracks." The length of each phage chromosome can then be measured by measuring the length of the photographic image composed of a row of a number of short tracks. In this photograph the chromosomes of T4 appear to be about 50μ long. Sixty-eight μ is the length of the total amount of DNA per phage calculated from the chemically measured nucleotide content of T4 and the dimensional parameters of the Watson–Crick DNA model. This photograph was kindly supplied by John Cairns. Magnification: 1,365×.

The hypothetical chromosome is composed of "separate" DNA molecules held together by internucleotide hydrogen bonding in regions of homologous base sequence. The difficulties in getting clear answers to this question are primarily technical (but partly semantic, as you can see). They include the following: (1) When backbone interruptions are found, they may be a consequence of a small amount of cleavage, perhaps enzymatic, resulting from the procedures by which the chromosome was extracted for study. (2) When studies fail to demonstrate backbone breaks, they may have done so because of *our* failure to understand fully the rather new techniques that are used to study giant polymers.

Chapter 8 discusses experiments that suggest the possibility of structures like those shown above and approaches to the demonstration of their existence (if they do exist). In general, we may expect that the extent of our uncertainty about chromosome structure increases with increasing chromosome size; things are at their worst when we discuss Chromosomes.

In the course of the phage life cycle, the DNA undergoes transitions from the condensed phase to the extended phase and vice versa. In the mature particle the DNA is condensed; throughout the intracellular phase extended DNA is present. Indeed, it is only in the extended phase that the DNA directs protein synthesis, duplicates, or undergoes genetic recombination (see Chapter 8). About halfway between the time of infection and the time of cellular lysis, mature particles containing condensed DNA appear in the infected cell.

Little is known about the mechanism of the transition of phage DNA from the extended form to the condensed form or its reverse. Careful electron microscopic examination of the components of mature particles and of the stages in phage maturation, however, adds detail to our knowledge of the sequence of events and permits educated speculation about some of the mechanisms.

At the time of infection the core in the phage tail probably penetrates the cell surface (see Fig. 2.5). It seems likely that the hole through the axis of the core then forms a canal between the interior of the phage head and the interior of the bacterial cell. The DNA might then "diffuse" from the region of high concentration through the canal into the bacterium. The only awkward point in this scheme is getting

Fig. 6.4. Condensed phage DNA in an infected bacterial cell. About midway in the infectious cycle DNA molecules of many phages undergo a transition from an extended phase to the condensed phase shown here in a longitudinal section of a single bacterial cell infected by T4. This photograph, kindly supplied by Eduard Kellenberger, appeared in *Virology,* 8 (1959), 488. Magnification: 41,000×.

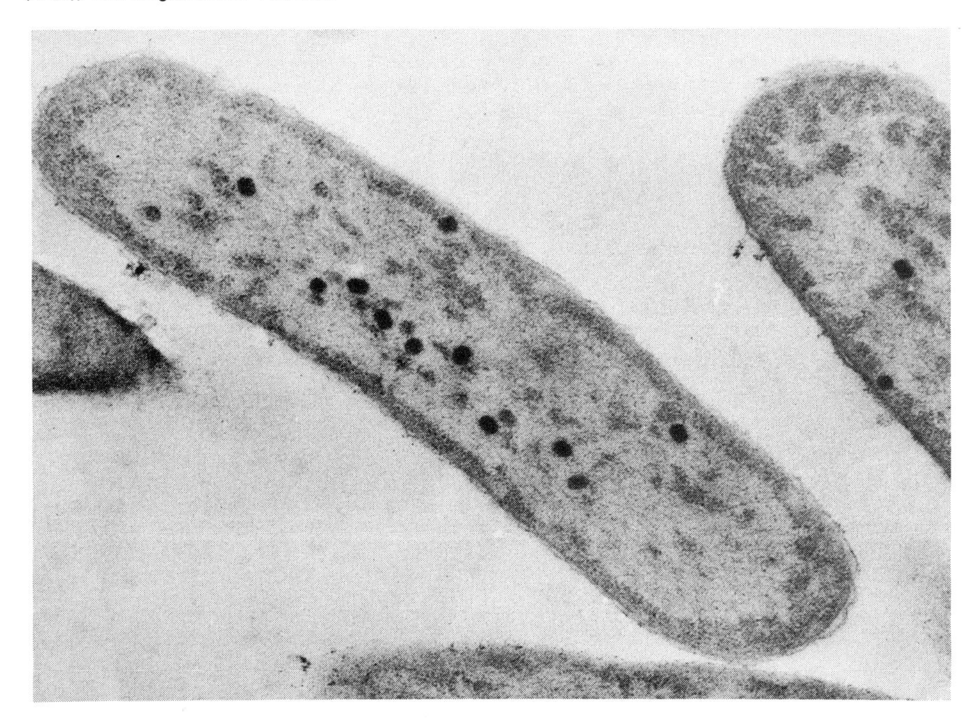

one end of the chromosome threaded into the very narrow (20-30Å diameter) hole. One may imagine that this was achieved as one of the steps in maturation of the particle in its previous host. Perhaps the core was assembled around one end of the chromosome.

As might be anticipated, condensation of the DNA does not represent a reversal of the above steps; the DNA is not "stuffed" into completed protein coats. Instead, it condenses into the shape of a bi-pyramidal hexagonical prism around which the subunits of the protein coat are laid down (see Fig. 6.4). The only clue we have to the mechanism of condensation is that some protein is required. Perhaps it is the protein that is found in small quantities inside the head of mature particles.

The bacterial chromosome

We have seen the evidence that the phage chromosome is as "one dimensional" as it can be; it has the thickness of a single DNA molecule of the Watson–Crick structure. There are reasons to suspect that the structure of bacterial chromosomes may be as simple, although the evidence is not quite as compelling. Figure 6.5 is an electron micrograph of the DNA released by gentle rupture of a bacterial cell. The failure to see ends suggests quite strongly that the chromosome has the same type of DNA arrangement as do phages. The question of the *number* of linearly arranged DNA molecules per chromosome is even more ambiguous for bacteria than for phages. DNA

Fig. 6.5. An electron micrograph of part of the DNA from a ruptured cell of the bacterium *M. lysodeiktikus.* The rarity of "ends" in the photograph suggests that the DNA is organized in one long unbranched structure. This photograph, kindly supplied by A. K. Kleinschmidt, appeared in *Z. für Naturforschung, 16b* (1961), 730. Magnification: 28,600×.

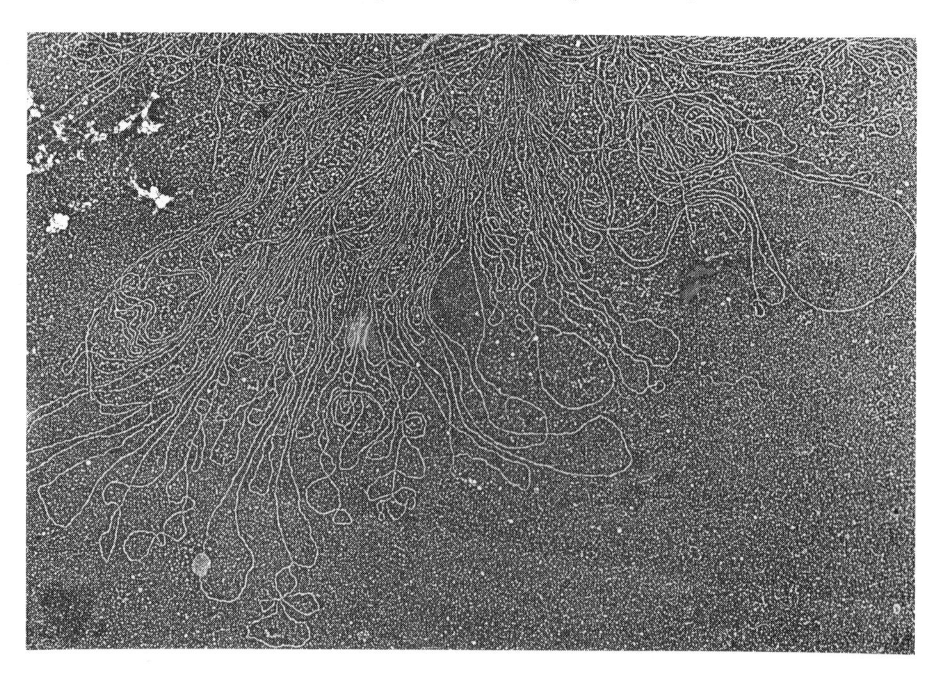

molecules of such length are so subject to lateral scission by the shear forces associated with even very careful laboratory manipulations that isolated chromosomes fail to stay in one piece long enough to answer many of the experimental questions put to them. The picture in Fig. 6.5 was obtained by opening a bacterium and gently spreading its DNA on an air-water interface before transferring it to an electron-transparent solid material for viewing. The notion of linearly arranged DNA molecules (one or more) is strengthened by the analysis of bacterial conjugation brilliantly conducted by François Jacob and E. L. Wollman.

Conjugation in *E. coli* involves the formation of a conjugation tube between members of opposite sex. The DNA of one of the nuclei of the "male" cell passes slowly through the tube into the "female" cell. Conjugation is completed upon rupture of the tube, which may occur either before or after all the DNA has been transferred. After a short lag, division of the female cell resumes. If the two cells undergoing conjugation differ by one or more distinguishable hereditary characteristics, the DNA transfer may have observable genetic consequences; descendents of the female exconjugant may manifest some of the transferred genetic markers. In Chapter 9 we shall examine in more detail the fate of the transferred DNA. For our present purposes, it is sufficient to note that transfer can be detected by its genetic consequences. The two experiments described below reveal that the genetic markers are located on a linear structure upon which no branches are detected and that the linear integrity of this structure depends upon the intactness of its component DNA. The results are fully compatible with the picture of the bacterial chromosome gained by direct observation.

Conjugation in bacteria can be interrupted at will by subjecting a suspension of conjugating cells to the shear forces created by rapid stirring. For any conjugating pair, the interruption of conjugation leads to the failure of some markers to be transferred; apparently the chromosome is broken along with the conjugation tube. In a population in which the onset of conjugation has been synchronized, the time at which each of the markers is transferred can be determined by artificially interrupting conjugation at various times, and scoring the female exconjugants for transferred markers. For a given male strain it is found that each of the many genetic markers studied has a unique time of transfer; i.e., each marker occupies a distinctive position on the chromosome, and markers are transferred in single-file procession. Data and further details of this experiment are given in Fig. 6.6.

Transverse cuts in the DNA of a male cell can be introduced by permitting the decay of P^{32} incorporated within the DNA. When the transferability of each of a number of markers is measured as a function of the average number of P^{32} decays, markers that are transferred early in conjugation are found to be relatively resistant to loss of transferability by P^{32} decay. Markers transferred late lose transferability at a relatively high rate. Further details of this experiment are given in Fig. 6.7. The primary conclusions to be drawn are twofold. (1) Genetic markers that have been separated from the leading end of the chromosome (the origin) prior to transfer fail to be transferred. (2) Scission of DNA results in scission of the chromosome.

The outcome of another kind of experiment is highly consistent with our view of phage and bacterial chromosomes as being single DNA molecules or, perhaps, an array of DNA molecules attached end to end. This experiment, which may take a variety of forms operationally, involves an examination of the distribution of labeled parental atoms between daughter nuclei in the case of bacteria or among progeny particles in the case of phages.

For phages, equilibrium density-gradient centrifugation of intact particles has been applied. The large percentage of DNA in phage particles and the stability of the particles in CsCl are responsible for the success of the approach. In the case of bacteria, autoradiography of daughter cells of uninucleate bacteria labeled in their DNA with H^3-thymidine has been successfully applied. When complications resulting from genetic recombination (see Chapters **8** and **9**) are accounted for or avoided, the genomes of both phages and bacteria are observed to be composed of two subunits that separate from each other at duplication and remain intact throughout subsequent generations; i.e., the chromosomes of both phages and bacteria act with respect to the distribution of atoms at duplication like single DNA molecules.

Chromosomes of higher organisms

In bacteria the separation of daughter chromosomes from each other prior to cell division can be observed microscopically (Fig. 6.8). It is obvious that for bacteria such direct visual observation is of little help in elucidating structure and behavior of chromosomes at the molecular level. The situation is somewhat better for many higher organisms. The Chromosomes, though more complicated in structure, are at least large enough to see clearly. As a consequence, the published observations on Chromosome appearance and behavior are staggering in number. Many of these observations have been casual; a few have derived from attempts to test predictions of hypotheses by experimentally altering the behavior or structure of the Chromosomes. This volume contains only those observations that are needed to understand an experiment by J. Herbert Taylor and his associates, the most compelling experiment to date on the organization of DNA in Chromosomes. The interesting Chromosomal alterations accompanying cellular differentiation are described in Hartman and Suskind's *Gene Action* and in Clement Markert's *Developmental Genetics*; variations in the numbers of Chromosomes within and among species are discussed in Lawrence Mettler's *Population Genetics and Evolution,* James Brewbaker's *Agricultural Genetics,* and Victor Mc-

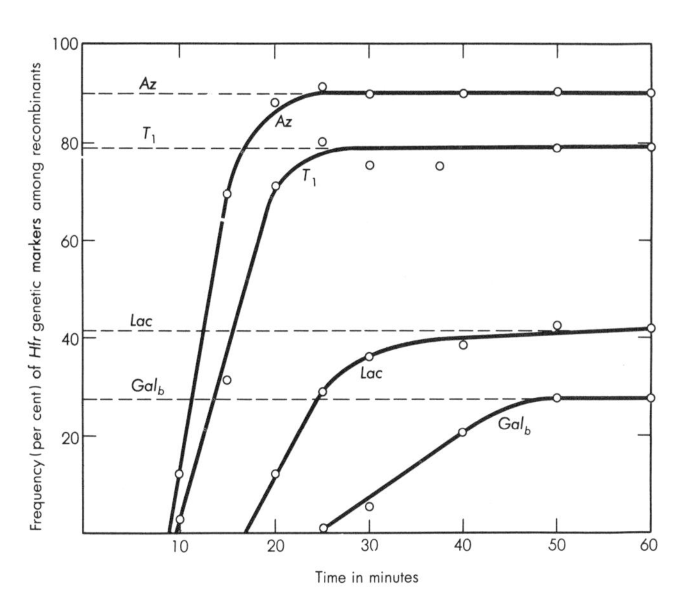

Fig. 6.6. The order of penetration of the genetic characters of the male strain K12 *Hfr* H of *E. coli* during conjugation. Male and female (K12 F^-) bacteria were mixed together under conditions permitting conjugation to occur. At intervals samples were removed and conjugation was interrupted by treatment with a blender. The samples were then spread on an agar-petri plate under conditions that permit the growth of certain descendants of the female exconjugants only. In order to grow, a cell must have one distinguishing hereditary characteristic of the F^- strain (resistance to streptomycin in this case); this ensures that it be a descendant of a female cell. In addition the cell must possess one (or more) hereditary characteristics of the *Hfr* strain; this ensures that the cell is indeed a descendant of an exconjugant. The hereditary abilities to make the amino acids threonine and leucine (T^+L^+) were selected for in this case. These two markers are known to be transferred very early (before 10 minutes) in this *Hfr* strain. The time-axis intercepts of the curves represent the times at which each of four other genetic markers are first transferred into some of the F^- cells. The final values achieved by the curves are determined in part by the likelihood of spontaneous interruption of conjugation and in part by events that occur after transfer (genetic recombination; see Chapter 9) and that can lead to the failure of transferred markers to be transmitted into the same daughter cells of the F^- exconjugant. This figure, reproduced by permission of François Jacob and E. L. Wollman, appeared in their *Sexuality and the Genetics of Bacteria*, rev. ed. (Academic, 1961).

Fig. 6.7. The effects of P^{32} decay occurring in the *Hfr* donor bacteria before transfer. *Hfr* H streptomycin-sensitive (S^s) bacteria were grown in a medium containing 70 mc./mg. of phosphorus, and samples were then frozen in liquid nitrogen. Every day a sample was thawed and mixed with F^- cells of the same streptomycin-resistant (S^r) auxotrophic strain employed in the experiment described in Fig. 6.6. After 1 hour at 37°C., samples were plated on selective medium. The proportions of $T^+L^+S^r$ recombinants (see Chapter 9) having one of the *Hfr* characters Az^s, T_1^s, Lac^+, Gal^+ are plotted on a logarithmic scale versus the time in days and the fraction of P^{32} atoms that have disintegrated. This figure, reproduced by permission of François Jacob and E. L. Wollman, appeared in their *Sexuality and the Genetics of Bacteria*, rev. ed. (Academic, 1961).

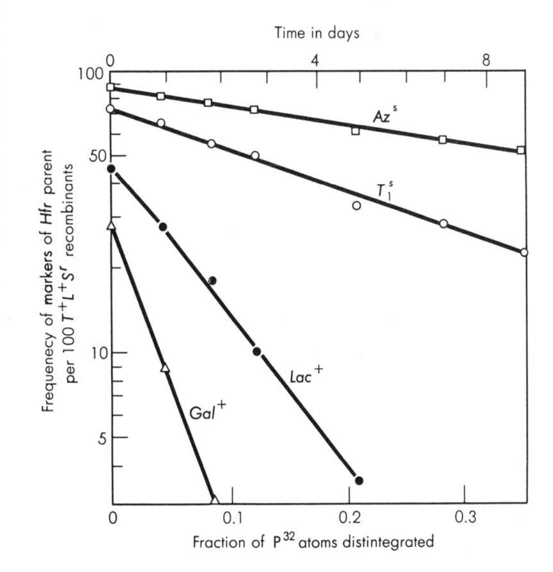

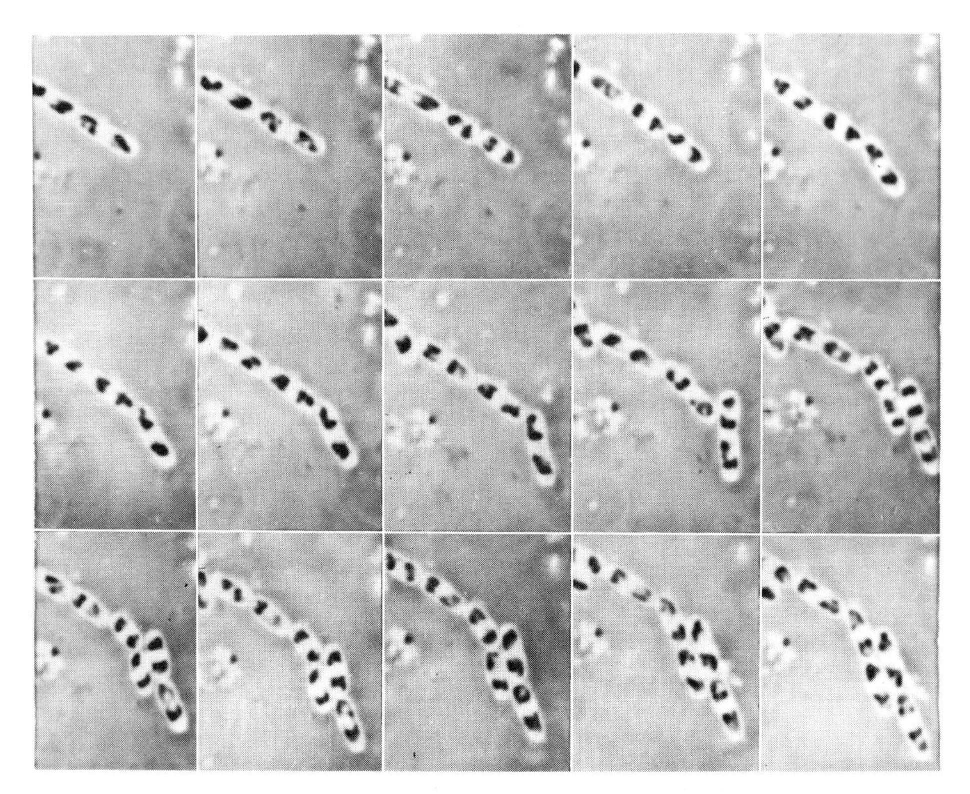

Fig. 6.8. Separation of daughter chromosomes in *E. coli* as viewed by time-lapse photomicrography. A small clump of cells growing with a generation time of 30 minutes was photographed at intervals under conditions of illumination that distinctly reveal the chromosomes (phase contrast microscopy). The array of photographs should be read "like a book," from left to right starting on the top line. The individual photographs were taken at the times (in minutes) indicated below (letting 0 be the time of the first frame):

0	6	12	21	30
33	36	39	48	54
57	60	66	72	75

These photographs were kindly supplied by D. J. Mason of the Upjohn Company, Kalamazoo, Michigan.

Kusick's *Human Genetics.* Carl Swanson's *Cytogenetics* is devoted entirely to the appearance and behavior of Chromosomes. Each of these books is a part of this series.

The Chromosomes are composed of DNA, RNA, and two classes of proteins in addition to smaller amounts of other substances. The role of the DNA in Chromosome function is clear from the studies of microorganisms—it carries the genetic information from generation to generation. Our present knowledge of how the information in the DNA is expressed (see *Gene Action*) permits us to identify the role of the RNA. The RNA is not to be thought of as an integral part of the basic structure of the Chromosome but as a family of polymers made under the direction of the DNA and destined for transfer to the cytoplasm where they are all-important in protein synthesis. Of the two classes of proteins, one (the histones) contains many basic amino acids and little tryptophan. These proteins are probably bound to the

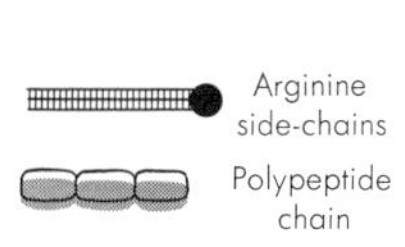

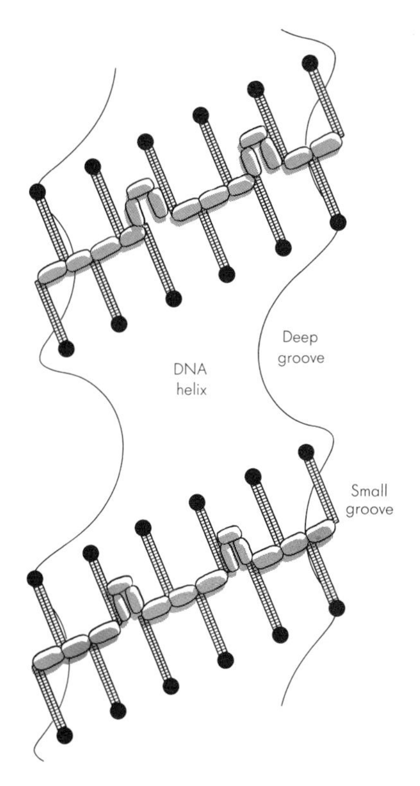

Fig. 6.9. Diagram showing the relationship between DNA and the basic protein protamine suggested by X-ray diffraction data. The small groove of the DNA molecule is occupied by the polypeptide chains that have a large number of basic residues. The amino groups of these residues lie close to the phosphate groups of the two DNA chains. Nonbasic amino acids in the protamine are accommodated by folds in the peptide chains. Protamines occur exclusively in the Chromosomes of the sperm of some species. The more common basic protein, histone, neutralizes the charged phosphate groups in the DNA of most other Chromosomes. X-ray diffraction data suggest that the histones occupy both grooves of each DNA molecule. This figure, reproduced by permission of Maurice Wilkins, appeared in *Cold Spring Harbor Symp. Quant. Biol., 21* (1956), 83.

DNA by ionic bonds. It is redundant to say that they serve to neutralize the phosphate groups of the DNA, which, at physiologic pH, are highly ionized, but at present no other role is known for them. The spatial relationship between DNA and basic protein as deduced from X-ray diffraction studies is shown in Fig. 6.9. The other, nonbasic, proteins are characterized by higher tryptophan content as well as by lower content of basic amino acids. Their only *known* role, as we shall see below, is to provide an additional degree of freedom for people who speculate on chromosome structure at the molecular level.

Each time a cell divides to become two cells, the two daughter cells are essentially identical to the mother cell; in particular, each daughter receives a full complement of Chromosomes. Two activities of the Chromosomes are thereby implied. (1) Chromosomes duplicate between cell divisions. (2) Daughter Chromosomes are parceled out to daughter cells so that each cell receives one full set of Chromosomes.

During most of the division cycle, Chromosomes are not visible as discrete entities; their DNA is in the elongated phase (Fig. 6.10a). During this period the DNA duplicates. The duplication can be detected, among other ways, by autoradiographically determining the time of incorporation of H^3-labeled thymidine. Subsequent to the completion of DNA duplication, condensation of the Chromosomes begins (Fig. 6.10b). As the Chromosomes become visible they can be

Fig. 6.10. A diagrammatic summary of the behavior of Chromosomes during mitosis. For clarity of illustration (both visual and conceptual) I have "selected" a haploid cell containing a complement of only two, nonhomologous chromosomes. This explanation is not logically necessary—I offer it to help the reader who may have encountered mitosis previously; the naïve reader is asked to ignore it.

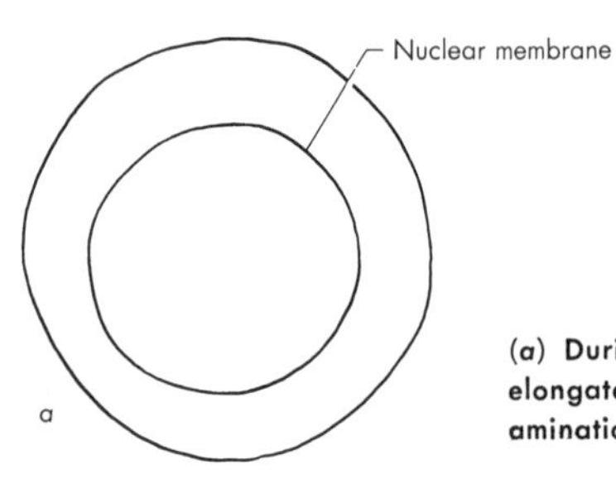

(*a*) During interphase, Chromosomes are typically so elongated as to be invisible to ordinary microscopic examination. DNA duplication occurs during this period.

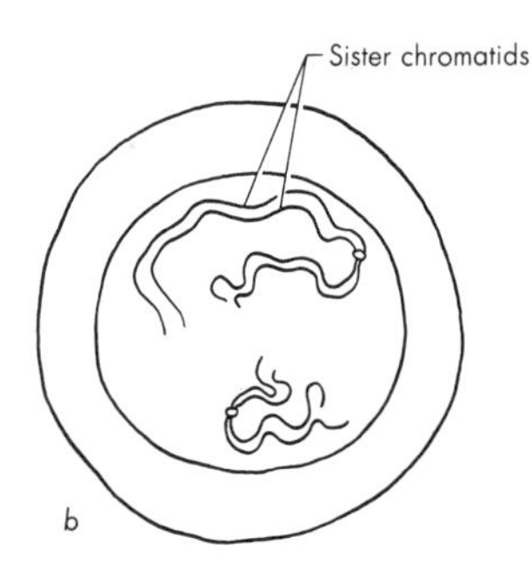

(*b*) The onset of prophase is signaled by a degree of Chromosomal condensation (shortening and thickening) that makes the Chromosomes visible. At this stage, each Chromosome is visibly composed of two longitudinal halves, the sister chromatids.

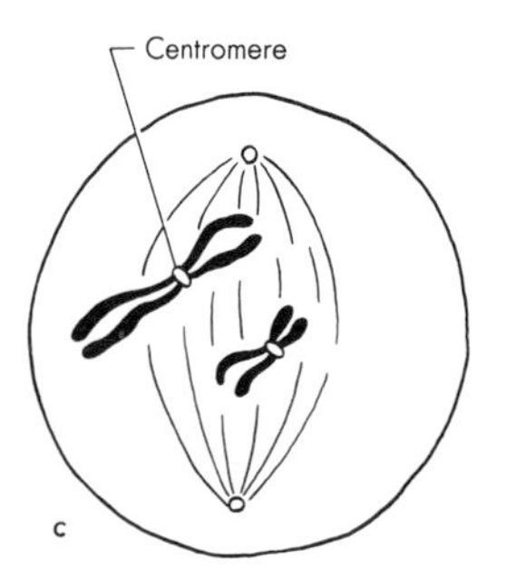

(*c*) The spindle apparatus, which is responsible for the orderly separation of the sister chromatids, appears as the nuclear membrane disappears and the Chromosomes continue to condense.

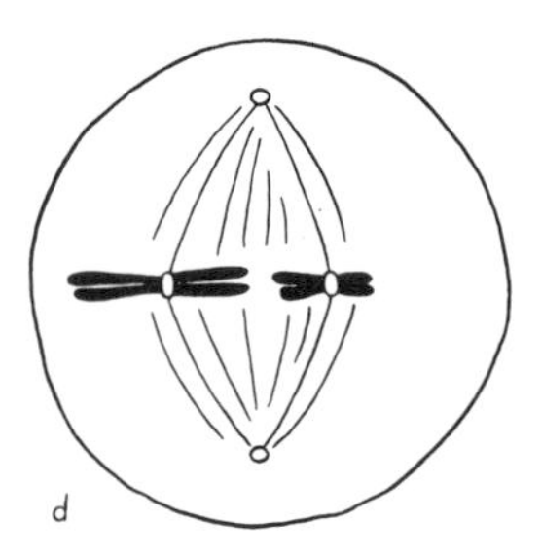

(*d*) In metaphase, the Chromosomes assume positions on the equatorial plane of the (three-dimensional) spindle apparatus. The centromeres appear to be connected to the two spindle poles by fibers of the spindle apparatus.

Fig. 6.10 (*cont.*)

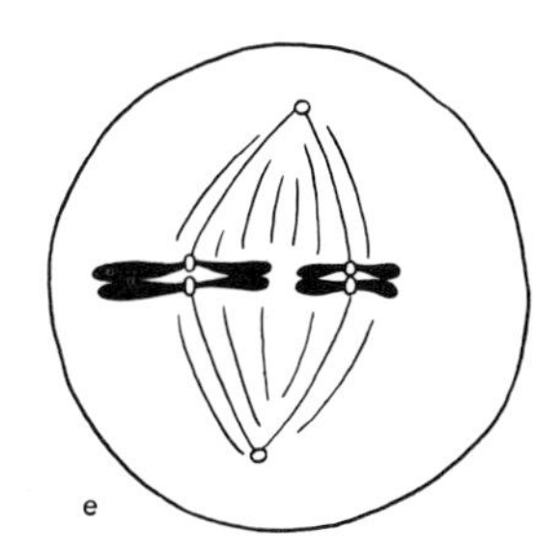

(e) The centromeres of each Chromosome divide.

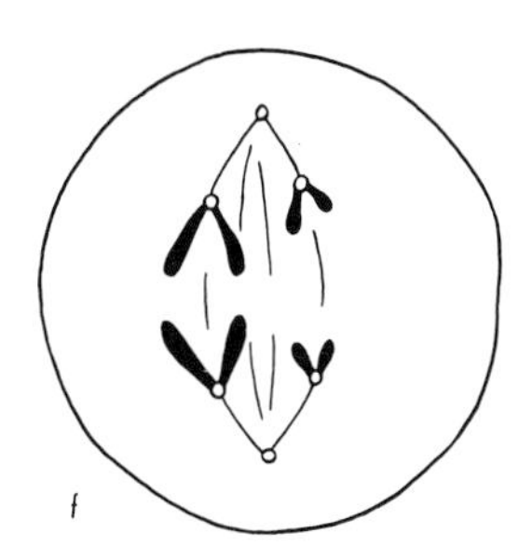

(*f*) In anaphase the daughter Chromosomes move to opposite poles, aided in their movement by the spindle apparatus.

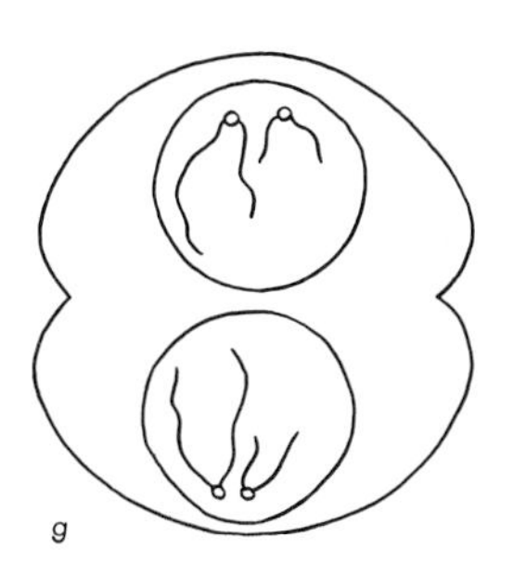

(*g*) The mitotic cycle is completed by re-entry into interphase. The spindle fibers disappear, the nuclear membrane reforms, and the chromosomes elongate. The early stages in this portion of the cycle are referred to as telophase. In most cases, cytoplasmic division follows nuclear division in such a way that the two cells each receive a nucleus containing identical sets of chromosomes.

seen to divide longitudinally; at this stage each Chromosome is composed of two chromatids. When condensation is well advanced, the nuclear membrane disintegrates and the spindle apparatus appears (Fig. 6.10c). The Chromosomes assume positions on the equatorial plane of the spindle axis (Fig. 6.10d). Spindle fibers appear to connect the centromere of each Chromosome to each of the two poles of the spindle. The centromeres become visibly double (Fig. 6.10e), and the two halves of each Chromosome move to the opposite poles of the spindle (Fig. 6.10f). The nuclear membranes reform, the spindle apparatus disappears, and the Chromosomes return to the elongated state (Fig. 6.10g). Nuclear division is followed by cytoplasmic division and the complete return of the nucleus to the interphase state. The conventionally identified "stages" in this process called mitosis are diagrammed, described, and named in Fig. 6.10.

The preceding description of mitosis is both simplified and generalized. It will suffice for our purposes, however.

J. Herbert Taylor and his associates studied the transfer of atoms of the DNA of Chromosomes to their daughter Chromosomes. DNA in the root tip of English broad bean (*Vicia faba*) seedlings was labeled with H^3 by exposing the growing root tip to a solution containing H^3-labeled thymidine. After about a third of a division cycle, the seedlings were transferred to a nonlabeling medium containing colchicine. The colchicine permits Chromosome duplication while blocking cytoplasmic division. After periods corresponding to one or two cell-generation times, seedlings were removed and the root tips fixed and pressed against photographic film. The electrons emitted upon the decay of the incorporated tritium are of such low energy that they produce images only immediately above their point of entry into the film. The level of labeling in each of the two chromatids of a metaphase Chromosome can therefore be separately determined. The film is developed while opposed to the pressed root tip; the Chromosomes and their autoradiographic images can be simultaneously viewed. The number of divisions undergone by a set of Chromosomes since the time of labeling can be determined by counting the Chromosomes. The Chromosomes in cells with 12 metaphase Chromosomes have not duplicated following the labeling. The Chromosomes in cells with 24 and 48 metaphase Chromosomes have duplicated once and twice respectively.

The Chromosomes in labeled nuclei undergoing their first metaphase since the period of labeling were equally radioactive in the two chromatids. The 24 Chromosomes in nuclei in their second postlabeling metaphase were radioactive in one chromatid only; the amount of label in the radioactive chromatid was equal to the amount present in each chromatid in the previous metaphase. In those cells with 48 Chromosomes, two of the sets of Chromosomes were completely unlabeled; the other two sets were labeled in the same fashion as the Chromosomes in cells that had undergone one less division. The reader should convince himself of the validity of Taylor's conclusion: "The chromosomes before duplication are composed of two units which extend throughout the length of the chromosome. The units separate at duplication and each has a complementary[2] unit built along it." In short, Chromosome duplication is semiconservative.

Taylor's experiment is summarized in Fig. 6.11. Color it now. The Chromosomes duplicate semiconservatively, so don't color them red. Use magenta for the labeled chromatids; color the nonradioactive chromatids yellow.

The actual arrangement of DNA in a Chromosome is as yet unknown. However, with respect to the transmission of atoms to daughters, Chromosomes duplicate as if they were single DNA molecules. The possibility that a single DNA molecule runs the entire length of a Chromosome would seem to be the model to rule out before expending too much thought on alternative schemes. Among the other schemes recently suggested, the favorites are those in which a number of DNA molecules are attached end to end by "linkers" of unspecified composition (or of nonbasic, tryptophan-containing protein). The "linkers" are

[2] The complementary character of the two Chromosomal units is deduced from the rules that apparently govern the (rare) "sister-strand" exchanges observed in these experiments (see Problem 6.4).

Fig. 6.11. The mode of distribution of the atoms of parental DNA into sister chromatids as revealed by the experiments of J. Herbert Taylor and his collaborators.

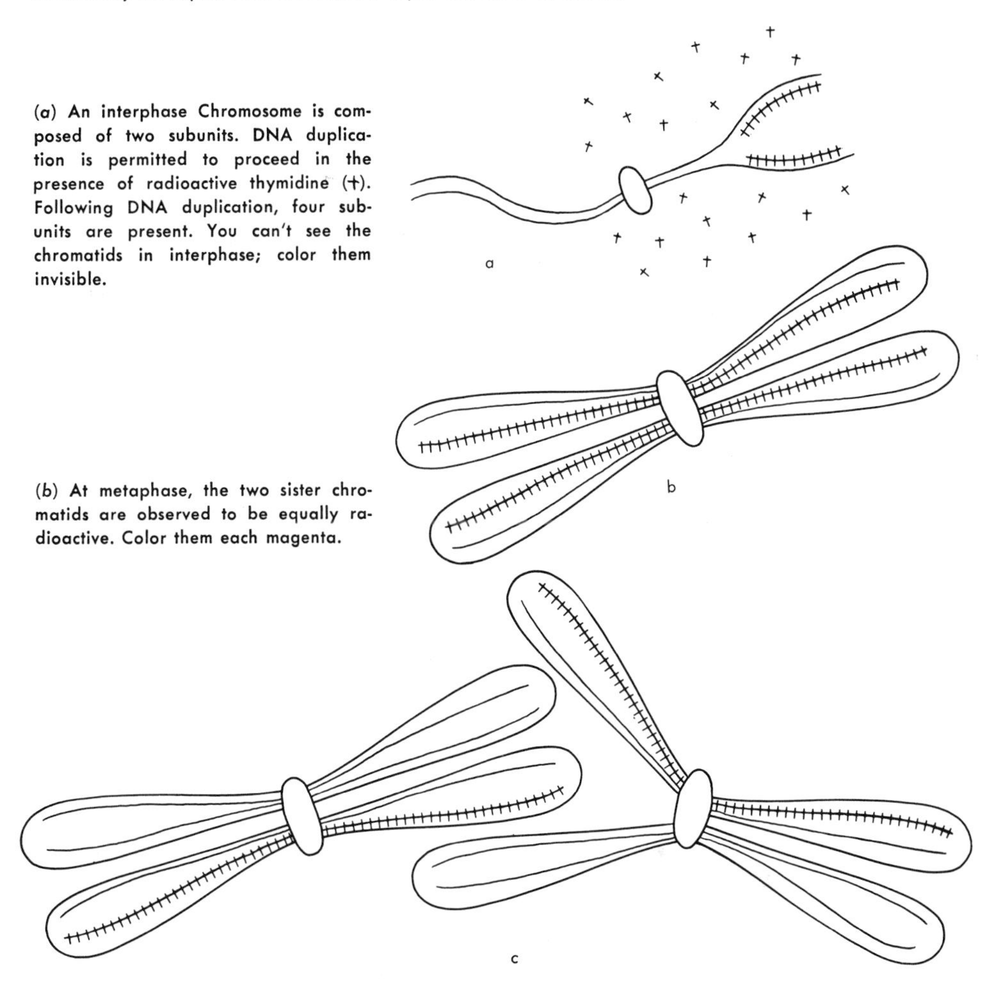

(*a*) An interphase Chromosome is composed of two subunits. DNA duplication is permitted to proceed in the presence of radioactive thymidine (+). Following DNA duplication, four subunits are present. You can't see the chromatids in interphase; color them invisible.

(*b*) At metaphase, the two sister chromatids are observed to be equally radioactive. Color them each magenta.

(*c*) If the cell undergoes a second mitosis (in the presence of colchicine in a nonradioactive medium), each of the daughter Chromosomes is observed to have one radioactive and one nonradioactive chromatid. Since the hot chromatid is observed to contain the same amount of label as did each of the chromatids in the previous metaphase, color them the same shade of magenta. Reflect upon the wonders of the Nuclear Age while you color the nonradioactive chromatids yellow. Quickly!

hypothesized to have two important properties. (1) They provide "joints" at which the Chromosome can bend permitting the DNA molecules to lie side by side. (2) The "linkers" are freely rotating so that any DNA molecule in the Chromosome can rotate along its helix axis without rotating all of the DNA molecules. This feature makes the untwisting of chains that accompanies DNA duplication easier to contemplate.

Summary

In this chapter we have posed the problem of how DNA is organized within chromosomes. We have consciously ignored most of the efforts of the cytologists and cytochemists who have been at this problem for years. Their evidence is usually difficult to evaluate and often conflicting. (See Swanson's *Cytogenetics* for a brave try.) A direction in which answers should be sought, however, is clearly indicated by the semiconservative nature of duplication of genic material at the viral, bacterial, and higher organism levels of organization.

A completely independent approach to the question of chromosome structure is afforded by studies of genetic recombination, to which we turn in Chapters **7**, **8**, and **9**.

References

De Robertis, E. D. P., W. W. Nowinski, and F. A. Saez, *General Cytology*, 3rd ed. Philadelphia: W. B. Saunders Co., 1960. A delightful classic in the field of cellular structure.

Jacob, François, and E. L. Wollman, *Sexuality and the Genetics of Bacteria*. New York: Academic Press, Inc., 1961. Chapters IX and XII are pertinent here, but all the chapters should be read eventually.

Taylor, J. Herbert, "The Time and Mode of Duplication of the Chromosomes," *Am. Naturalist, 91* (1957), 209-21. A clear, economically presented review of chromosome duplication with appropriate emphasis on the remarkable experiments of its author.

Thomas, C. A., Jr., "The Organization of DNA in Bacteriophage and Bacteria," in *Molecular Genetics*, Vol. I, J. Herbert Taylor, ed. (New York: Academic Press, Inc., 1963), pp. 113-51. An up-to-date review of the evidence bearing on the structure of phage and bacterial chromosomes.

Problems

6.1. (a) If the chromosome of *E. coli* duplicates at the same rate per nucleotide as does the DNA of phage T2 (see Problem 4.3b), how much time is required for duplication? Compare your answer with the generation time of *E. coli* (20 minutes in nutrient broth at 37°C.). (b) How much time would be required to duplicate the DNA of *Drosophila* if we suppose that each of the *Drosophila* Chromosomes duplicates from one end to the other and that each of the chromosomes duplicates during the same period?

6.2. An *E. coli* culture of streptomycin-resistant males was grown in a medium containing one P^{32} atom per 1,000 P atoms. Part of the P^{32}-labeled culture was mated with streptomycin-sensitive female cells. The zygotes from these matings were frozen immediately after transfer of the DNA into the zygote. Similarly, the remainder of the male culture was frozen and stored. At intervals samples of the zygotes were thawed and the number of zygotes in a sample giving rise to streptomycin-resistant offspring was determined. At the same times, samples of the male culture were thawed and mated with streptomycin-sensitive females. The number of zygotes giving rise to streptomycin-resistant offspring was determined for these zygotes also. The following data were obtained:

Number of zygotes giving streptomycin-resistant offspring

Fraction of P^{32} *atoms decayed*	*Zygotes formed after* P^{32} *decay*	*Zygotes before* P^{32} *decay*
0	1034	1006
0.2	226	942
0.4	47	912
0.6	12	851
0.8	3	826

(For the zygotes formed before decay the slight disappearance of zygotes giving streptomycin-resistant offspring presumably reflects damage to DNA interfering with the incorporation of donor DNA into the chromosome of the recipient.) How many nucleotide pairs exist in the genetic structure between the origin and the locus under study? (Take the quantum efficiency for DNA rupture by P^{32} decay as 0.1.)

6.3. Using your answer from Problem 6.2, calculate the time elapsing in a conjugation between the passage of the origin and the part of the chromosome conferring streptomycin resistance from the male to the female cell. Assume that 10^3 nucleotide pairs are transferred per minute.

6.4. Chromosmes in root-tip cells of *Bellevalia* were labeled with H^3-thymidine. The roots were exposed to radioactive thymidine for a period sufficiently brief that no cells underwent more than one cycle of DNA duplication in the presence of label. The roots were then immersed in colchicine so that the number of postlabeling mitosis for each cell could be determined by chromosome counting.

Among cells which have undergone a post-labeling mitosis, an occasional chromosome is found that looks like this:

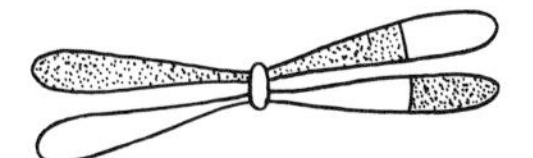

(The shaded portions indicate the presence of H^3.) These chromosomes appear to have exchanged homologous parts of sister chromatids. Sometimes one chromosome like the one above is found in a cell (call it a single exchange); sometimes *both* members of a pair of daughter chromosomes show the effects of exchange at the same level (call it a twin). A twin looks like this:

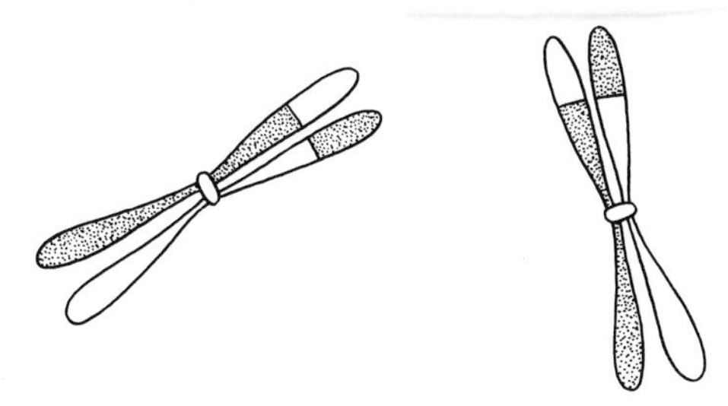

Let's focus on one Chromosome that is permitted to duplicate in the presence of tritiated thymidine.

(a) At the first metaphase following labeling, how many of the two sister chromatids will be labeled with H^3?

(b) The two sister chromatids break at the same level and exchange parts shortly after labeling.

(1) How many of the two sister chromatids will appear nonuniformly labeled at the first postlabeling metaphase? (Assume that the two subunits in each chromatid break at the same point and that these two subunits remain attached to each other throughout.)

(2) How many of the four daughter chromatids at the second postlabeling metaphase will appear nonuniformly labeled if at the time of the exchange new (H^3) subunits always rejoin with old (H^1) subunits?

(3) How many of the four daughter chromatids will appear nonuniformly labeled if at the time of the exchange new (H^3) subunits always rejoin with new (H^3) subunits?

(4) How many of the four daughter chromatids will appear nonuniformly labeled if at the time of the exchange one of the exchanged pieces rejoins new to old and old to new while the other rejoins new to new and old to old?

(c) From chromatid exchanges occurring prior to the first metaphase what will be the ratio of singles to twins at second metaphase if rejoining of the exchanged parts is at random with respect to the age of the subunits?

(d) If a chromatid exchange occurs between the first and second metaphase, will it produce a single or a twin?

(e) What will be the ratio of events (detectable or not) occurring just prior to second metaphase to those occurring prior to first metaphase?

(f) At second metaphase,

(1) What will be the ratio of singles to twins if reunion is always old to old and new to new?

(2) What will be the ratio of singles to twins if reunion of exchanged parts is at random with respect to age of subunits?

(3) What will be the ratio of singles to twins if reunion is always old to new and new to old?

Taylor found a ratio of singles to doubles at second metaphase of about 2 : 1. The ratio was clearly less than 10 : 1. This result suggests that the rules governing reunion of chromatid subunits following exchange of a length of chromatid is such that old subunits always reunite with the new subunits of the sister chromatids. This rule suggests that the two subunits of a chromatid are not identical but are instead complementary. This evidence furthers the view that the subunits of a chromatid are the single chains of one DNA molecule or a linear array of DNA molecules.

(g) Suppose that chromatid exchange does *not* occur but that events of the following sort occur: Sister chromatids occasionally break at the same level and the subunits are rejoined at random with respect to age *without* any exchange between the two chromatids. What will be the single to twin ratio observed at second metaphase?

This situation that derives without chromatid exchange and with assumed *identity* of subunits mimics chromatid exchange with nonidentity of subunits. Thus an independent demonstration of chromatid exchange is needed, but seems to be lacking at this time.

Recombination in Higher Organisms

In Chapter 2 we saw that a culture derived from a bacterial cell transformed from property X (say penicillin sensitivity) to property Y (say penicillin resistance) does not contain DNA that can transform Y cells to X. A bacterial cell can carry the DNA responsible for property X *or* property Y but generally not both. These two states of the bacterial chromosome are mutually exclusive alternatives; they are allelic to each other.

We have seen in Chapter 6 that the parts of a chromosome that affect each of a number of properties of a creature are located at distinctive places on a chromosome. When two creatures differ by a single mutation we shall call the distinctive bit of DNA in either of them a marker. The mutant marker is an allele of the original bit of DNA. Members of a set of alleles occur as mutually exclusive alternative markers at a distinctive locus on a chromosome.

When penicillin-sensitive, lactose-negative bacteria are exposed to DNA from penicillin-resistant, lactose-positive cells, the cells are transformed to drug resistance or to ability to ferment lactose but only occasionally to both states. If a drug-resistant, nonfermenting transformant is cultured, the DNA extracted from it can transform other cells to resistance (but not to sensitivity) and to the inability to ferment lactose (but not to the ability to ferment). A symmetric statement can be made regarding the drug-sensitive, lactose-positive transformants. Such transformed cells each have a chromosome not exactly like that of either the recipient or the donor strain but derivable by recombination of the genic material of the two strains.

We have abstracted the results of experiments on bacteria into a set of interrelated definitions in terms of the structure of the genic material set forth in Chapters 1 to 6. In the discussion to follow there will not often be the opportunity to remind you of these definitions—in fact, the words will frequently be used without reference to either DNA or chromosomes. The formalisms of recombination analysis are self-contained; by completely independent logic and techniques they lead to a picture of a chromosome delightfully harmonious with the concept we have thus far developed.

Meiosis

Recombination requires that the genic material (or parts of it) from two or more different individuals be brought into intimate association. In higher organisms this is achieved by the processes of nuclear fusion and meiosis. These processes are conveniently described as they occur in the unicellular green alga *Chlamydomonas*. The appendix that follows this chapter is a report by James Kezer on experiments involving these processes in salamander spermatocytes. The photomicrographs in the appendix are keyed to the diagrams of the corresponding stages of meiosis shown in Fig. 7.1.

Each *Chlamydomonas* cell contains one genome composed of a number (about 8) of nonhomologous Chromosomes; i.e., the cells are haploid (or monoploid). The creature propagates by mitosis; one act of mitosis followed by cell cleavage gives two independent *Chlamydomonas* cells. Under certain conditions, primarily related to the nutritional state of the cells, cells of opposite mating type unite in pairs. Fusion of the two cells is followed by fusion of the nuclei. Soon thereafter the DNA of the Chromosomes duplicates, and the Chromosomes become visible[1] in the leptotene stage of the prophase of meiosis (Fig. 7.1a).

The Chromosomes look different from the way they look in the early prophase of mitosis; in fact, in many creatures, each Chromosome *appears* to be composed of but one chromatid; i.e., even though the DNA has duplicated (as determined chemically) there is often no visible sign that the Chromosomes have duplicated.[2] Homologous

[1] In *Chlamydomonas* meiosis is difficult to see because of the small size of the Chromosomes. The generality of the phenomenon of meiosis, however, leaves no doubt about the essential applicability of this description.

[2] Because the Chromosomes at meiosis look and behave differently from the way they do at mitosis one wonders whether the DNA of the Chromosomes behaves differently during meiosis. Do the Chromosomes in the premeiotic interphase duplicate semiconservatively with respect to their DNA as they do prior to mitosis? Are the chains of individual DNA molecules separated from each other into daughter molecules as

Chromosomes then enter into intimate pairing in the zygotene stage (Fig. 7.1b). The pairing (synapsis) begins often at one end of each pair of homologous Chromosomes and proceeds "zipperwise" to the other end. A synapsed pair of homologues is called a bivalent. The Chromosomes shorten and thicken, and each Chromosome divides longitudinally into two chromatids at the pachytene stage of meiotic prophase (Fig. 7.1c). In diplotene (Fig. 7.1d) the homologous Chromosomes appear to repel each other, but are typically held together by one or more chiasmata (the singular form is *chiasma*). These chiasmata *give the appearance* of having resulted from breakage, exchange, and reunion between a pair of chromatids, the two members of which are from different Chromosomes in the synapsed Chromosome pair.

The Chromosomes shorten and thicken and chiasmata often appear to move to the ends of the Chromosomes in the meiotic prophase stage called diakinesis. The nuclear membrane disappears and the pairs of Chromosomes held together by terminalized chiasmata assume positions on the equatorial plane of the spindle apparatus at metaphase I. Homologous centromeres with attached chromatids move to opposite poles of the spindle in anaphase I (Fig. 7.1e). The nuclear membranes form and the cell divides in telophase I. Each of the daughter cells then enters a period of interkinesis (an "interphase" without DNA synthesis; Fig. 7.1f) during which the Chromosomes become more or less elongated. This period is followed by shortening and thickening of the Chromosomes in prophase II. The Chromosomes, each composed of two chromatids, move to their respective equatorial planes in metaphase II. Centromeres divide and the two chromatids of each Chromosome move to opposite poles in anaphase II (Fig. 7.1g). The nuclear membranes reform and each cell divides. Four haploid cells (Fig. 7.1h) are the products of the meiosis.

Following the completion of meiosis in *Chlamydomonas,* the spore case opens and the four cells, each free-swimming like the cells that originally fused, are liberated. The life cycle of *Chlamydomonas* is summarized in Fig. 7.2.

Segregation

In *Chlamydomonas* the two mating types are called mt^+ and mt^-. A given cell is of either one mating type or the other. When a *Chlamydomonas* cell divides, each of the daughter cells is of the same mating type as the parent. Mating type is "inherited." Among the four products of meiosis, two are almost invariably found to be of one mating type and two of the other. The two mating types, which are mutually exclusive, alternative properties, are manifested by the mei-

they are in mitotic duplication? Experiments aimed at answering both of these questions have been and are being tried; to date there are no conclusive results. The strongest statement that can be made now is that there seems to be no reason for doubting the semiconservative nature of all DNA and Chromosome duplication.

Fig. 7.1. A diagrammatic summary of the behavior of Chromosomes during meiosis.

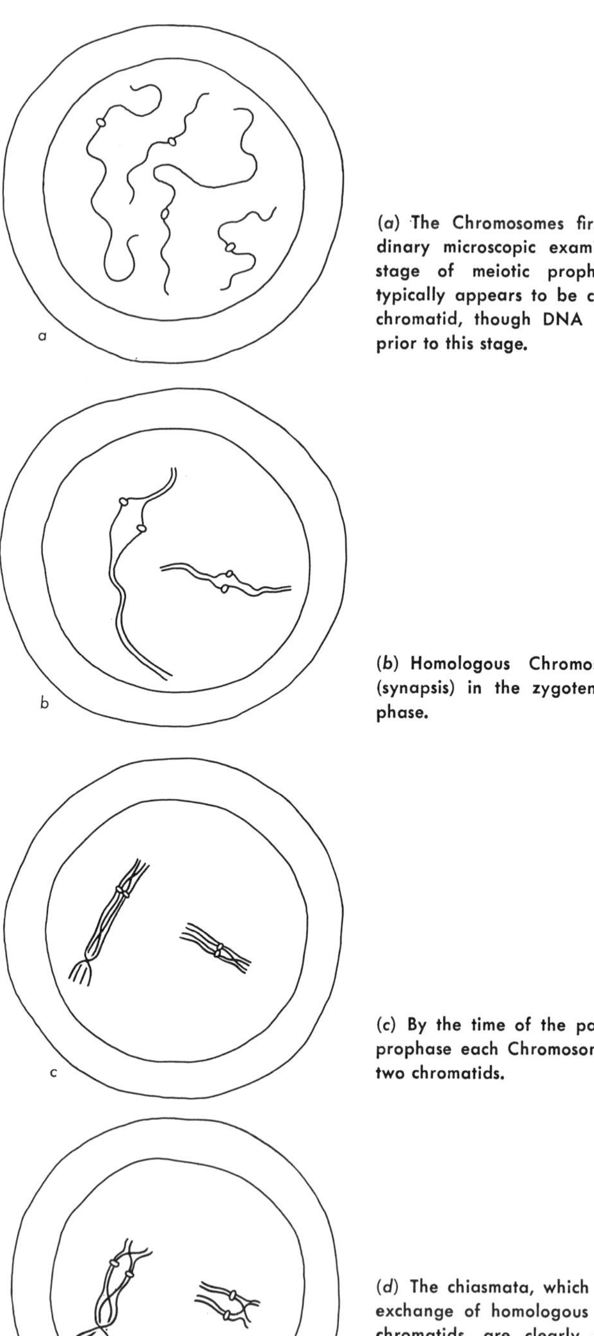

(*a*) The Chromosomes first become visible to ordinary microscopic examination in the leptotene stage of meiotic prophase. Each Chromosome typically appears to be composed of but a single chromatid, though DNA duplication has occurred prior to this stage.

(*b*) Homologous Chromosomes undergo pairing (synapsis) in the zygotene stage of meiotic prophase.

(*c*) By the time of the pachytene stage of meiotic prophase each Chromosome is visibly composed of two chromatids.

(*d*) The chiasmata, which look as if they arose by exchange of homologous parts between synapsed chromatids, are clearly visible in the diplotene stage of meiotic prophase.

Fig. 7.1 (*cont.*)

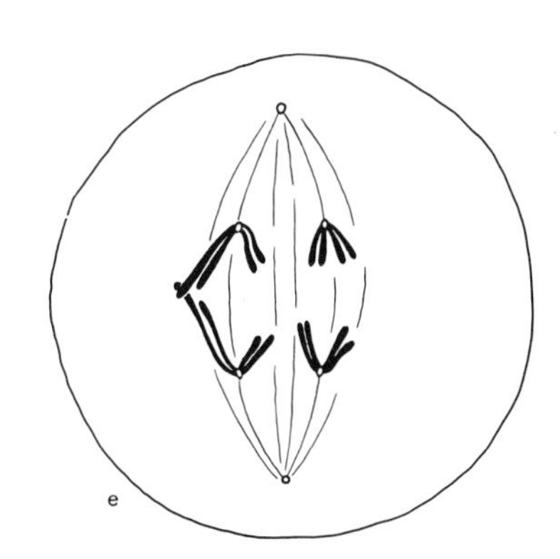

(*e*) Following the orientation of the bivalents (synapsed pairs of homologous Chromosomes) on the equatorial plane of the spindle apparatus in metaphase I, the homologous centromeres move toward opposite poles of the spindle in anaphase I.

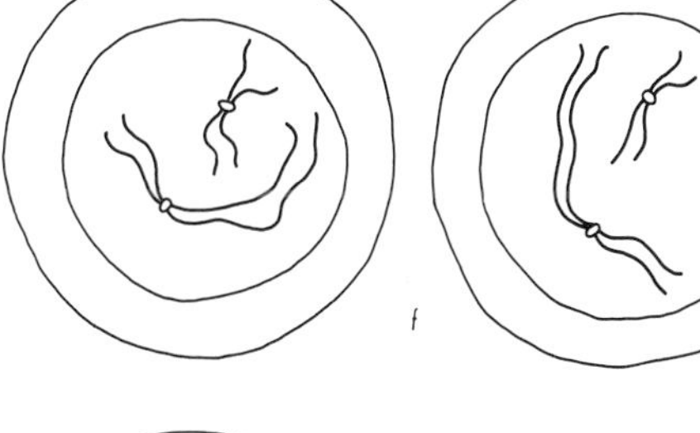

(*f*) Reformation of the nuclear membrane is followed by cell division in telophase I. In interkinesis, the Chromosomes may become more or less elongated.

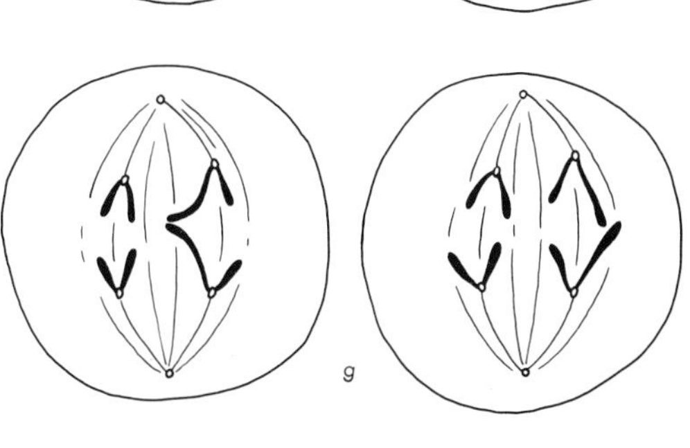

(*g*) The second meiotic division is initiated by shortening and thickening of the Chromosomes in prophase II followed by migration of the Chromosomes to the equatorial plane of the spindle apparatus in metaphase II. Centromeres "split" and homologous chromatids move toward opposite poles of the spindle in anaphase II.

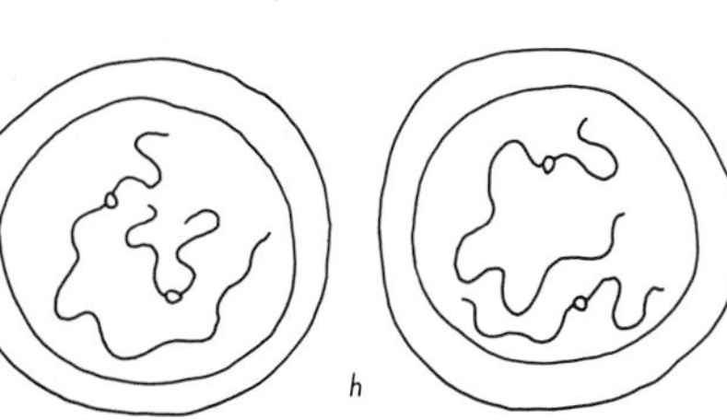

(*h*) A second telophase results in the formation of four haploid cells, the final products of meiosis.

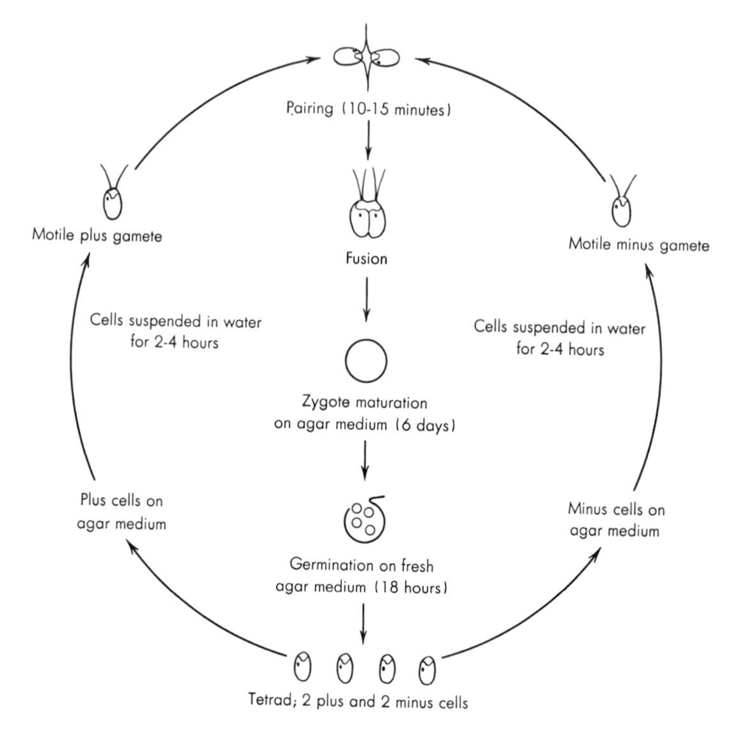

Fig. 7.2. The life cycle of *Chlamydomonas*. Under appropriate conditions, haploid unicellular individuals of opposite mating types fuse in pairs. Nuclear fusion is followed by DNA duplication and meiosis within a spore case. The four haploid products, two of each mating type, are released upon germination of the (zygo)spore. This figure, reproduced by permission of Paul Levine, appeared in *Cold Spring Harbor Symp. Quant. Biol., 23* (1958), 102.

otic products *as if* they were determined by allelic markers, i.e., as if they were determined by factors that segregate from each other at meiosis as do the homologous points of chromosomes.

A number of mutant *Chlamydomonas* strains have been isolated through the use of techniques comparable to those described for bacteria in Chapter 1. Fusion and meiosis (mating) between mutant cells of one mating type and wild-type cells of the other mating type typically show the same phenomenon of **2 : 2** segregation. Two of the four products of each meiosis are wild type (like one of the parent cells) and the other two are mutant like the other parent.

Recombination

When mating occurs between *Chlamydomonas* cells differing by two or more hereditary properties (call this event a cross) the haploid products are frequently not all like one parent or the other with respect to all of the hereditary characteristics. We must conclude that the markers determining the various characteristics undergo recombination during meiosis.

Let's use symbols for the markers that differentiate the two parents in a cross. Let's call one parent ab^+ by which we mean that it carries a mutant marker at locus a and a wild-type marker at locus b. We may then call the other parent a^+b. The products of meiosis can be of four types:

$$\left.\begin{matrix} ab^+ \\ a^+b \end{matrix}\right\} \text{ parental types}$$

$$\left.\begin{matrix} a^+b^+ \\ ab \end{matrix}\right\} \text{ recombinant types}$$

It follows as a consequence of the 2 : 2 segregation of each of the pairs of alleles that among the four products (a tetrad) of any given act of meiosis

the number of ab^+ cells = the number of a^+b cells

and

the number of a^+b^+ cells = the number of ab cells

Thus, three kinds of tetrads can occur:

ab^+	ab^+	a^+b^+
ab^+	a^+b	a^+b^+
a^+b	a^+b^+	ab
a^+b	ab	ab

We can call them respectively

parental ditype tetrad (P)	tetratype tetrad (T)	recombinant ditype tetrad (R)

For crosses performed under standard conditions and involving a particular pair of loci the frequencies with which each of the three types of tetrads occurs is a reproducible characteristic property of that *pair* of loci. For most higher organisms, including *Chlamydomonas*, the most commonly encountered situation is that the frequency of P's equals the frequency of R's, and these two kinds of tetrads together make up a fraction of the total which is characteristic of that pair of markers. Since P's contain only products of parental type, R's contain only recombinants, and T's contain equal numbers of both types, these crosses give haploid products exactly half of which are recombinant. Markers behaving in this fashion are said to be unlinked. The equal frequency of P's and R's for unlinked markers can be simply understood if those markers are presumed to be situated at loci on *different* (non-homologous) chromosomes and if the orientation on the spindle at metaphase I of each bivalent were random. The *occurrence* of T's, however, is not accounted for by these correct, but inadequate, assumptions. They can be understood, on the other hand, if the chiasmata observed in meiotic prophase *do* reflect exchange between chromatids attached to separate homologous centromeres (non-sister chromatids). Convince yourself that a chiasma occurring in one bivalent between the marked locus and the centromere would be sufficient to account for the occurrence of tetratype tetrads. The study of exchange between chromatids is facilitated by the existence of pairs of *linked* loci.

Not all crosses give 50 per cent recombinant types, however; occasionally, pairs of loci are found that give less. Such loci are said to be linked to each other. Vigorous collection of mutants and measurement of recombinant frequencies in many of the possible crosses involving two loci (two-factor crosses) reveal that groups of linked loci exist. Loci within any one group (a linkage group) are all demonstrably linked to each other (or to a common locus), whereas no linkage is demonstrable between any two loci in different linkage groups.

Crossing over

As a rule, the data on recombinant frequencies between pairs of markers within a linkage group can be represented in the form of a one-dimensional linkage map. To construct a map, each marker is represented by a point in space. Two markers that show low frequencies of recombination with each other are located close together; markers giving large frequencies are put farther away from each other. When a number of markers have been located, the geneticist generally finds that he can draw one and only one nonbranching line from point to point (until all points lie on the line) such that the distance from one point to another *along the line* is invariably larger for markers that show large recombination values than for those showing smaller values.

The consistent success with which such efforts to construct one-dimensional maps have met suggests that the loci *do* exist on one-dimensional structures; the obvious candidates for the structures underlying the maps are the Chromosomes. The events leading to recombination between linked markers are called crossovers.

In crosses involving linked loci, tetratype tetrads are observed. It is clear therefore that crossing over cannot be accounted for solely by events occurring prior to the meiotic duplication of the genic material. Rather it *appears as if* crossing over at any one level occurs between only two of four "strands." It seems likely that the "strands" are the four chromatids in each bivalent at prophase I and that the chiasmata are cytologically visible manifestations of crossing over.

The conclusion that crossing over occurs in the four-strand stage raised a set of complex problems: (1) Can any chromatid cross over with any other chromatid in a given set of four homologous chromatids? (2) Does the choice of chromatids engaging in crossing over at one level in the paired Chromosomes influence the choice at any other level? These questions have not been answered in a fully satisfactory fashion, but Problems 7.5 and 7.6 outline some of the evidence and the steps in the reasoning that leads to two tentative views: (1) Sister chromatids (the two chromatids resulting from the duplication of one Chromosome) do not cross over with each other. (2) The choice of chromatids engaging in crossing over at any one level has no influence on the choice at any other level; there is no chromatid interference.

The mapping function

The existence of one-dimensional linkage maps suggests that the frequency of recombinants for a given pair of loci is positively correlated with their physical distance apart on the Chromosome. This relation would follow if crossing over could occur at many different places along the paired Chromosomes. The quantitative relationships between recombination and crossing over can be examined from a study of measurements of the recombinant frequencies between pairs of loci for which the map sequences have been determined.

Granted the assumption of no sister-strand crossing over, all the tetrads arising from bivalents in which one cross-over occurs will be tetratype. For bivalents with two crossovers in the marked region there are three ways in which the two crossovers may occur: (1) the two crossovers may involve the same two chromatids (in which case they are said to be regressive); (2) the two crossovers may involve one common chromatid only (progressive); (3) the two crossovers may involve completely different pairs of chromatids (digressive). These cases are diagrammed in Fig. 7.3. The members of a regressive pair of exchanges cancel each other and thereby produce a parental ditype tetrad. A progressive pair produces tetratype tetrads. A digressive pair of exchanges produces recombinant ditype tetrads. Since we have supposed an absence of sister-strand crossing over and of chromatid interference, these types will arise in the ratio

$$\tfrac{1}{4}\mathrm{P} : \tfrac{1}{2}\mathrm{T} : \tfrac{1}{4}\mathrm{R}$$

For three exchanges the ratio will be

$$\tfrac{1}{8}\mathrm{P} : \tfrac{3}{4}\mathrm{T} : \tfrac{1}{8}\mathrm{R}$$

(Convince yourself!)

In general, whatever the number of exchanges (greater than 0), P equals R. Since P's contain only products of parental type, R's contain only recombinants, and T's contain equal numbers of both types, it follows that the frequency of recombinants among tetrads with one or more crossovers between two marked loci will be $\frac{1}{2}$.

We are now able to write a null hypothesis that relates the average number of crossovers between two marked loci with the frequency of recombinants. Let us *assume* that among the bivalents the numbers of crossovers are distributed according to the Poisson expression (see appendix on Poisson distribution). This assumption is equivalent to the assumption that the presence of one crossover neither increases nor decreases the likelihood of a second crossover; crossovers are assumed to be independent events. (We shall see later that this is rarely true.) Then, if the average number of crossovers between two marked loci is called x, the fraction of bivalents with no crossovers between the marked loci is $\dfrac{x^n e^{-x}}{n!}$ evaluated at $n = 0$, or, simply, e^{-x}. The fraction of bivalents with one or more crossovers between the marked loci is,

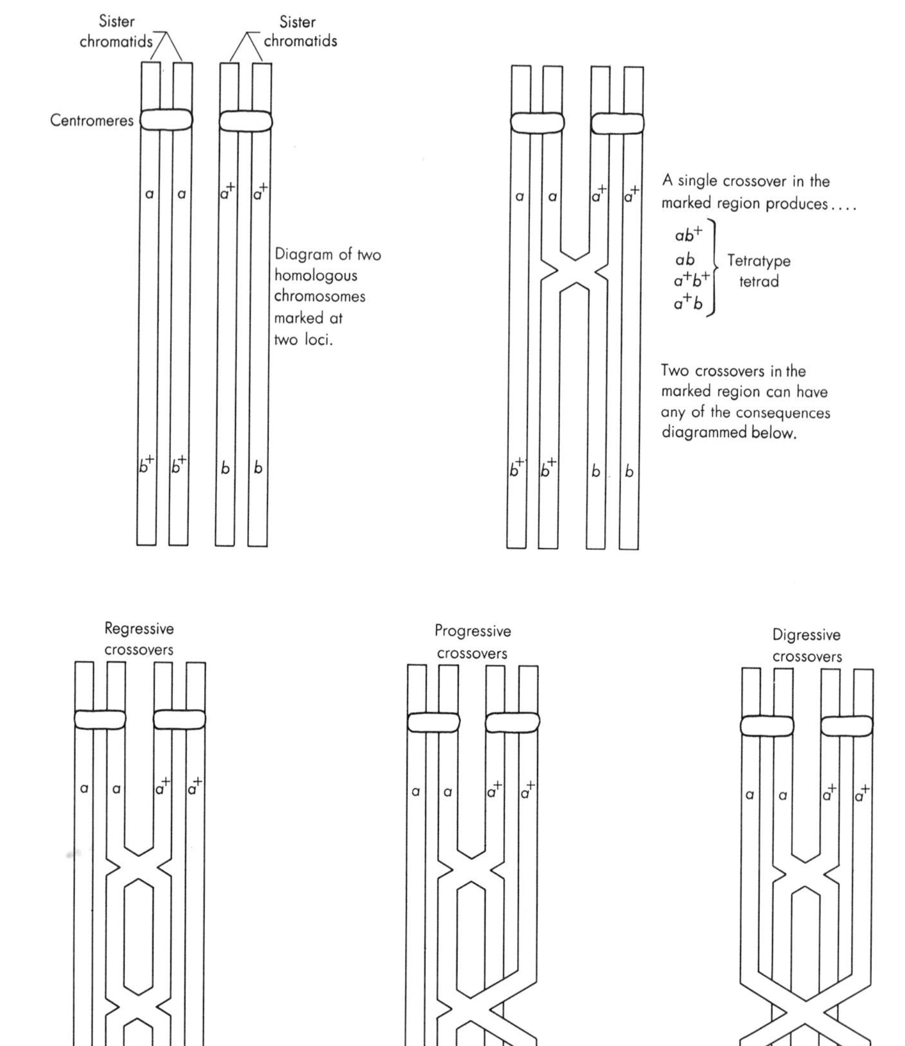

Fig. 7.3. The manner in which two crossovers can dispose themselves in a bivalent. In the presumed absence of sister-strand crossing over, three distinguishable arrangements of two crossovers are possible. The three arrangements and their recombinational consequences are diagrammed in the figure.

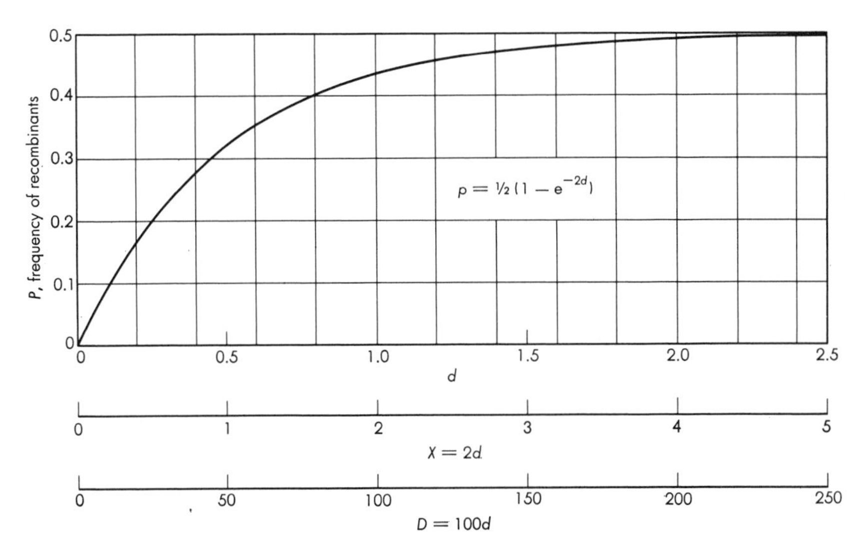

Fig. 7.4. The mapping function for recombination in higher organisms in the absence of interference. The recombinant frequency (*p*) increases linearly with map distance (*D*) at short distances. At long distances the recombinant frequency asymptotically approaches 0.5 and widely separated markers then appear to be "unlinked." The three metrics on the abscissa refer to Eqs. 7.3, 7.1, and 7.4 respectively.

therefore, $1 - e^{-x}$, and the frequency of recombinants is

$$p = \tfrac{1}{2}(1 - e^{-x}) \qquad \text{(Eq. 7.1)}$$

Whenever x is small ($<< 1$), $(1 - e^{-x}) = x$ (approximately), and

$$p = x/2 \text{ (approximately, when } x \text{ is small)} \qquad \text{(Eq. 7.2)}$$

We wish now to define the "distance" d between two loci such that d is proportional to x and for closely linked loci is equal to p. Assuming Eqs. 7.1 and 7.2 we can write $d = x/2$ and

$$p = \tfrac{1}{2}(1 - e^{-2d}) \qquad \text{(Eq. 7.3)}$$

If we now define a *map* distance as $D = 100d$, we can write

$$p = \tfrac{1}{2}(1 - e^{-2D/100}) \qquad \text{(Eq. 7.4)}$$

Equations 7.1, 7.2, and 7.4 are plotted in Fig. 7.4.

An inspection of Fig. 7.4 reveals several properties of an "ideal" map.

(1) Throughout the range where the curve is approximately a straight line with a slope of one, recombinant frequencies equal "distance" and are, therefore, additive. For three closely linked loci, 1, 2, and 3 linked in that order, the recombinant frequency from a cross involving 1 and 3 equals the sum of the recombinant frequencies from the two crosses involving 1 and 2 and 2 and 3 respectively.

(2) In the range where the curve has appreciable curvature, recombinant frequencies are not additive. When the map distances between three linked loci 1, 2, and 3 are rather large, the frequency of recombinants from a cross involving 1 and 3 is less than the sum of the recombinant frequencies from the two crosses involving 1 and 2 and 2 and 3 respectively.

(3) When map distances between markers are very large, the frequency of recombinants is independent of map distance and equals $\frac{1}{2}$.

Departures from the ideal mapping function

With most organisms the recombinant frequencies depart to some degree from the "ideal" mapping function of Fig. 7.4. If our assumptions regarding the absence of sister-strand crossing over and chromatid interference are correct, these departures must represent inadequacies in our assumption of a Poisson distribution of crossovers among bivalents.

For any trio of linked markers, departures from ideality, if they exist, can be detected as follows. Recombinant frequencies for each of the crosses 1×2, 2×3, and 1×3 are measured experimentally. These recombinant frequencies are then converted to "ideal" map distances. This conversion can be made conveniently by reading from the graph in Fig. 7.4. The map distances are then tested for additivity; the map distance between loci 1 and 3 is compared with the sum of the map distances between 1 and 2 and 2 and 3 respectively. If recombinant frequencies *do* depend on map distance in an ideal fashion, the derived map distances will indeed be additive.

Additivity may fail, however, for either of two reasons: the "ideal" map distance between loci 1 and 3 may come out to be either greater than *or* less than the sum of the two map distances for loci 1 and 2 and 2 and 3 respectively. In most higher organisms, systematic deviations of this sort are commonly found. For rather large recombinant frequencies the calculated map distance for loci 1 and 3 is typically greater than the sum of the calculated map distances for the other two pairs of loci. For extremely small recombinant frequencies, on the other hand, additivity of the calculated map distances usually fails in the other direction.

Three-factor crosses

A quantitative measure of the deviations from a Poisson distribution of crossovers among synapsed homologues can be conveniently expressed in terms of the frequencies of types arising from a cross involving three marked loci (a three-factor cross) all of which are linked to each other. Call the three loci 1, 2, and 3, and let them be marked by the alleles a and a^+, b and b^+, c and c^+ respectively. If the two parental types are abc and $a^+b^+c^+$, then the emerging types and their designations may be written as follows:

$$
\begin{array}{lll}
 & \left.\begin{array}{l} abc \\ a^+b^+c^+ \end{array}\right\} & \text{parental} \\[1em]
\text{recombinants for loci 1 and 2} = p_{12} & \left.\begin{array}{l} ab^+c^+ \\ a^+bc \end{array}\right\} & \text{recombinants for loci 1 and 2 only} \\
 & \left.\begin{array}{l} ab^+c \\ a^+bc^+ \end{array}\right\} & \text{double recombinants} \\
\text{recombinants for loci 2 and 3} = p_{23} & \left.\begin{array}{l} abc^+ \\ a^+b^+c \end{array}\right\} & \text{recombinants for loci 2 and 3 only}
\end{array}
$$

(The first two groups together are the recombinants for loci 1 and 2 $= p_{12}$; the last two groups together are the recombinants for loci 2 and 3 $= p_{23}$. The groups "recombinants for loci 1 and 2 only" and "recombinants for loci 2 and 3 only" together are the recombinants for loci 1 and 3.)

If crossovers are Poisson distributed, then recombination for loci 1 and 2 and for loci 2 and 3 will be statistically uncorrelated events. Under this condition, the frequency of double recombinants would be $p_{12} \times p_{23}$. We may define S, the coefficient of coincidence, by the equation

$$S = \frac{\text{Actual frequency of double recombinants}}{p_{12}p_{23}} \qquad \text{(Eq. 7.5)}$$

Then, simply by rewriting Eq. 7.5 we get

$$\text{Actual frequency of double recombinants} = S\, p_{12}p_{23}$$

The frequency of recombinants for loci 1 and 3 may then be written in terms of p_{12}, p_{23}, and S as

$$p_{13} = p_{12} + p_{23} - 2S\, p_{12}p_{23} \qquad \text{(Eq. 7.6)}$$

We see that S can be estimated experimentally either from the results of three-factor crosses by application of Eq. 7.5 or from the pooled results of each of the three two-factor crosses by application of Eq. 7.6. Values of S less than 1 mean that there is a tendency for adjacent pairs of loci not to undergo simultaneous recombination. Such an experimental result would suggest that crossovers tend to interfere with each other. Values of S greater than 1 would mean that adjacent pairs of loci undergo simultaneous recombination more often than would be expected if crossovers were Poisson distributed among synapsed homologues.

In the discussion above it was noted that calculated "ideal" map distances for moderately linked markers fail to be additive because D_{13} as estimated from the ideal mapping function is greater than the sum of D_{12} plus D_{23}. This statement is equivalent to the statement that

$$p_{13} > p_{12} + p_{23} - 2p_{12}p_{23}$$

which implies $S < 1$. As mentioned above, the actual magnitude of S for any linked trio of marked loci can be experimentally determined.

A formal model for recombination

For very close loci (say, less than 0.1 per cent recombinant frequency), S values greater than 1 are typically observed! There is as yet no satisfactory explanation for these phenomena of positive interference ($S < 1$) and negative interference ($S > 1$), but several models that give partial explanations have been put forth. Before we consider these models and the evidence that bears on them, let us construct our own model, which we shall make as simple as possible but adequate to explain the facts so far put forth in this chapter.

We shall suppose in our model that crossovers come in "clusters." Let's further suppose that the number of crossovers in each cluster is an odd number often greater than one. Loci that are far apart relative to the length of a cluster will recombine as a result of an odd number of clusters falling between them. Positive interference results from supposing that the presence of one cluster decreases the likelihood of finding another cluster nearby. Perhaps the mechanical properties of the Chromosomes are such that they cannot entertain two regions of "effective pairing" close together. We would diagram a synapsed pair of Chromosomes like this

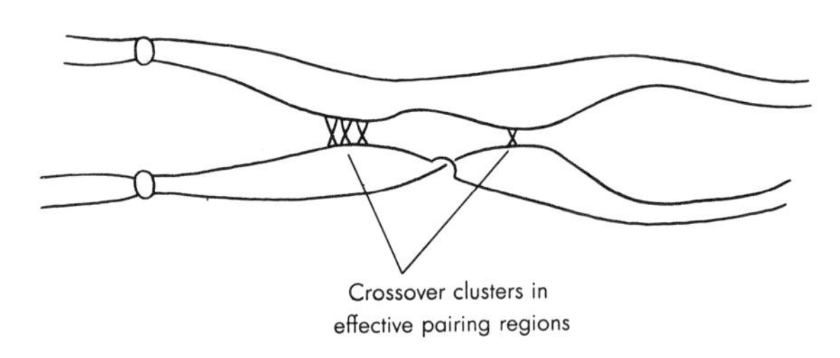

For loci close together relative to the length of an effective pairing region, crossing over occurs as a consequence of an odd number of crossovers falling between the loci. Negative interference is a direct result of the assumption of clusters. A four-factor cross of the following type provides information that leads us to modify our model.

Call the parents Xa^+bY and $X'ab^+Y'$ where loci a and b are very close together and X and Y are more or less equidistant from a and b

and give, say, 5 per cent recombinants in crosses with either a or b. Thus, X and Y are far from a and b relative to the length of the cluster, but they are close enough so that clusters seldom fall between them. In crosses of this sort as typically performed, the mutant markers a and b are alterations of the Chromosome that result in auxotrophy for a given nutrient. Therefore, the rare a^+b^+ recombinants arising in the cross are easily detected as the only meiotic products that grow on unenriched medium. A typical result of the cross is that among the a^+b^+ recombinants all four types with respect to loci X and Y are found in appreciable frequency. The presence in appreciable frequency of the parental types XY and $X'Y'$ requires that clusters containing even numbers of crossovers occur with about the same frequency as do clusters with an odd number of crossovers. Among a^+b^+ individuals from crosses of the above type, one recombinant (XY') is present in greater frequency than the other ($X'Y$). This result argues that the average number of crossovers per cluster is not very large. On the basis of these observations we may write a modified version (version II) of our model with three features: (1) crossovers come in clusters; (2) there is positive interference in the disposition of clusters along the Chromosome; (3) the number of crossovers per cluster is sometimes odd and sometimes even with a mean number of, say, 1, 2, or 3.

Version II *does* provide an adequate framework for thinking about the primary observations on the interference relationships in crosses with close and distant markers respectively. The experiments described below, however, clearly show that the model, though an adequate formalization for some purposes, is still oversimplified.

Nonreciprocal recombination

Individual tetrads from crosses of the type $Xa^+bY \times X'ab^+Y'$ have been examined. (Such analyses have been carried out primarily in the fungus *Neurospora*.) Since loci a and b are very close together, many tetrads must be studied to find a few that contain the a^+b^+ recombinant. These rare tetrads typically manifest violations of the rule of 2 : 2 segregation! For instance, a tetrad that contains the a^+b^+ recombinant often fails to contain the ab recombinant. In these tetrads the markers at loci X and Y, however, segregate in the normal ratio so that tetrads of the following sort may be observed:

$$\begin{array}{l} Xa^+bY \\ Xa^+b^+Y' \\ X'ab^+Y \\ X'ab^+Y' \end{array}$$

The other kinds of tetrads that involve 3 : 1 segregation for the close recombining loci but 2 : 2 segregation for the loose ones are also found.

Whenever two of the members of the tetrad are recombinant for X and Y, the a^+b^+ member is generally one of them. These findings lend detail to our knowledge of crossing over but have not as yet lent us *understanding* of that event.

Let's summarize the facts of crossing over as we now see them. Recombination for close markers is often nonreciprocal; it gives other than 2 : 2 segregations at one or the other of the two loci. Geneticists tend to refrain from ascribing this recombination to "crossing over" since recombination for loose markers, which *does* generally give reciprocal products in any one tetrad, has been ascribed to "crossing over." However, the recombination for close markers is so strongly correlated with recombination of markers on either side that we are strongly tempted to seek a common explanation for reciprocal and nonreciprocal recombination. There seems to be, however, no easy way to amend version II of our "cluster" hypothesis to explain these results. In fact, the results shed some doubt on our picture of crossing over as a process that occurs in the first prophase stage of meiosis. DNA synthesis precedes meiotic prophase, but the 3 : 1 segregations seem explicable only if DNA synthesis occurs within the region of a "cluster." Either of the following two explanations seems possible.

(1) Some crossing over *does* occur or is conditioned by events that occur during the period of DNA synthesis. If this is true we must chide ourselves for having relied upon the cytologists' description of meiosis.

(2) Crossing over occurs *after* Chromosome replication but an extra little bit of DNA synthesis occurs during prophase in the region of a "cluster."

There is hope that the near future will bring experimental results that can distinguish these alternatives.

Summary

In most higher organisms the genic material is organized into more than one Chromosome. Recombination of allelic markers at different loci can, therefore, come about in either of two ways. Markers at loci on different Chromosomes assort independently as a consequence of the random orientation of bivalents at the metaphases of meiosis. Markers at two loci on the same Chromosome recombine by crossing over or by a nonreciprocal process that seems intimately related to crossing over.

A description of crossing over in terms of the structure of the genic material (i.e., the DNA) is not yet possible. We don't know in detail how the DNA is organized in the Chromosomes, and we don't know the relationships between crossing over and DNA synthesis. We shall see in the next chapter that the viruses may be more promising experimental tools for studying the details of genetic recombination (although no very clear picture has yet come from those studies).

Our lack of knowledge of the mechanism(s) of recombination does not, however, prevent us from constructing linkage maps. The one-dimensionality of these maps argues that the genic material in a Chromosome is either in the form of one long DNA molecule or a one-dimensional array of DNA molecules.

References

Barratt, R. W., Dorothy Newmeyer, D. D. Perkins, and Laura Garnjobst, "Map Construction in *Neurospora crassa*," *Adv. Genet.*, *6* (1954), 1-93. From tetrad analysis and analysis of random meiotic products the authors develop mapping functions for *Neurospora*. The functions, which relate tetratype tetrad frequencies or recombinant frequencies with map distance, take into account the existence of interference. Mathematically inclined students might enjoy and profit from this paper.

Mitchell, M. B., "Aberrant Recombination of Pyridoxine Mutants of *Neurospora*," *Proc. Nat. Acad. Sci. U.S.*, *41* (1955), 215-20. By analysis of tetrads, the author showed that recombination between very close markers was accompanied not only by negative interference but also by 3 : 1 segregation ratios.

Sturtevant, A. H., "The Linear Arrangement of Six Sex-linked Factors in *Drosophila*, as Shown by Their Mode of Association," *J. Exp. Zool.*, *14* (1913), 43-59. Reprinted in *Classic Papers in Genetics*, J. A. Peters, ed. (Englewood Cliffs, N.J.: Prentice-Hall, Inc., 1959), pp. 67-78. A great little paper on the construction of a linkage map from data on recombinant frequencies.

Taylor, J. Herbert, "The Replication and Organization of DNA in Chromosomes" in *Molecular Genetics* (New York: Academic Press, Inc., 1963), pp. 65-111. A thoughtful attempt to account for the behavior of chromosomes in terms of a hypothesized arrangement of DNA within them.

Problems

7.1. Suppose we throw into a pot a large number of *Chlamydomonas* haploid cells of one genotype (e.g., able to synthesize nicotinamide) and an equal number of cells unable to make nicotinamide (*nic*−) and of the opposite mating type. The two *nic* markers behave as alleles. Cell and nuclear fusion is allowed to occur. The resulting cells are diploid. We now perform the following experiments on this pot.

(a) We remove a single diploid cell, permit meiosis to occur, and examine the 4 haploid products. How many are *nic*+?

(b) We remove 10 diploid cells, permit meiosis to occur, and examine all 40 emerging products. How many are *nic*−?

(c) We permit the very large number of diploid cells in the pot to undergo meiosis and we let the haploid products swim about until the contents of the pot are randomized. We pick one cell at random. What is the probability that it is *nic*+?

7.2. (a) What four kinds of meiotic (haploid) products can be produced by a diploid cell that contains the alleles A and a and the alleles B and b?

(b) Assume that the diploid cell in Problem 7.2a arose from the union of two haploid cells of genotypes AB and ab respectively.

(1) Cf the 4 kinds of meiotic products, which are "parental" and which are "recombinant"?

(2) In an experiment, suppose that the following numbers of meiotic products are counted:

AB	221	aB	64
ab	232	Ab	66

What is your estimate of the recombinant frequency from a cross involving the loci a and b? To how many "ideal" units does this correspond?

(c) Suppose the diploid cell in Problem 7.2b2 is also segregating the alleles C and c.

(1) How many genotypes of meiotic products can be produced? Specify them.

(2) Suppose that the frequency of recombinants for loci b and c is 20 per cent and for a and c is 38 per cent. What is the map sequence of the loci? Calculate the coefficient of coincidence for the regions ab and bc. In a three-factor cross involving loci a, b, and c, what frequency of double recombinants would you expect to find?

7.3. Occasionally, pieces of one Chromosome can become attached to the end of another Chromosome or even become inserted into another Chromosome. Such an event is a translocation. Suppose two loci a and b are known. A piece of another Chromosome has become inserted into the region between a and b. Crosses in which neither parent carries the translocation give 25 per cent recombinants for the loci a and b. Crosses in which both parents carry the translocation give 38 per cent recombinants for the same two loci. If you assume the applicability of the "ideal" mapping function, what is the map length of the translocated piece of Chromosome?

7.4. Following X-irradiation, aberrant Chromosomes can be found in increased frequency. "Ring" Chromosomes are found in which the two ends of one Chromosome have fused to each other so that the Chromosome looks like this:

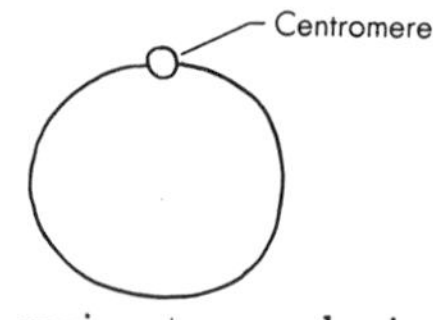

During meiosis in a cell carrying two such ring Chromosomes (and no normal homologue), the rings synapse with each other and undergo crossing over in the four-strand stage. At anaphase I, any bivalent in which one of the chromatids has engaged in an odd number of non-sister-strand exchanges gets "hung up" since the homologous centromeres are connected to each other. An odd number of sister-strand exchanges would be expected to show such "bridges" at anaphase II, but bridges at anaphase II do not seem to occur. What does this tell us about sister-strand crossing over?

7.5. (a) Assume that no crossing over between sister chromatids can occur. Among chromatid tetrads in which *one* crossover between two loci has occurred, what frequency of tetratype spore tetrads will result?
(b) Assume that sister chromatid crossing over is just as likely to occur as any other kind.
(1) Among tetrads in which *one* crossover has occurred between loci, what frequency of tetratype tetrads will result?
(2) Among tetrads in which 2 (or 3, or 4) crossovers have occurred, what frequency of tetratype spore tetrads will result if there is no chromatid interference? if there is complete positive chromatid interference? [3]
(c) In fact, situations are found in which there are more than 66.7 per cent tetratype tetrads. What does this tell us about sister-strand crossing over and chromatid interference?

7.6. In some fungi of the order Ascomycetes, meiosis proceeds in a long thin sac (ascus). The nuclei can seldom slip past each other so that the terminal member at either end of a tetrad and the cell next to it are sister cells of the same second meiotic division. This situation permits the recognition of recombination between marked loci and the centromere. Suppose a locus is marked by the alleles a and a^+.

If recombination has not occurred, the sequence of markers in the tetrad will be either aaa^+a^+ or a^+a^+aa.
(a) What will be the relative frequencies of these two types of tetrads?

If recombination has occurred, it *may* result in the appearance of tetrads with different marker sequences, e.g., aa^+aa^+ or a^+aaa^+. Such sequences indicate that the alleles a and a^+ have, because of crossing over, segregated in the second meiotic division. Assume the validity of the notion that there is no sister-strand crossing over and no chromatid interference.
(b) Suppose that in a particular bivalent *one* crossover has occurred between locus a and the centromere. What is the probability that the tetrad will manifest second division segregation?
(c) Suppose exactly two crossovers have occurred between the locus a and the centromere. What is the probability that a and a^+ will segregate in the second division? if exactly three crossovers occur? if a vast number of crossovers occur?

Assume now that sister-strand crossing over does occur but again that there is no chromatid interference.
(d) What is the probability that the tetrad will manifest second division segregation if in a particular bivalent *one* crossover occurs between locus a and the centromere? if two or more crossovers occur?

Under what conditions using an Ascomycete might you rule out the combined hypothesis of sister-strand crossing over with no chromatid interference?

[3] Positive chromatid interference is the situation wherein an adjacent pair of crossovers tend to involve different chromatids. In the case of complete positive interference, two adjacent crossovers invariably involve no common chromatid.

7.7. Consider a four-factor cross of the type $Xa^+bY \times X'ab^+Y'$. Among many haploid products of meiosis the following types were observed to be present with the indicated frequencies. (A dot means the individuals were not scored for the marker at that locus.)

Type	*Frequency*
$X \cdot b^+ \cdot$	0.025
$\cdot \cdot b^+Y$	0.030
$X \cdot b^+Y$	1.0×10^{-4}
Xa^+b^+Y'	1.0×10^{-6}
$X'a^+b^+Y$	4.0×10^{-7}
Xa^+b^+Y	6.0×10^{-7}
$X'a^+b^+Y'$	8.0×10^{-7}

Calculate S, the coefficient of coincidence characterizing simultaneous recombination in the following pairs of intervals: (a) Xb and bY, (b) Xa and ab, (c) ab and bY. NOTE: It is generally true and always fair to assume, in the absence of information to the contrary, that complementary types are present in equal frequencies among a large number of meiotic products. (Complementary types are those that carry different alleles at every one of the examined loci, e.g., the types $X'a^+b^+Y$ and $XabY'$.) This assumption is equivalent to the assumption that the frequencies of types are determined only by the positions of the loci and not by any other property of the markers themselves.

Appendix to Chapter 7

Meiosis in Salamander Spermatocytes

by James Kezer
Department of Biology, University of Oregon

The large size of salamander Chromosomes and the ease with which they can be prepared for observation make these amphibians ideal as a source of cells for the study of the meiotic process. The photomicrographs on pages 106-14 show the events of meiosis as they occur in salamanders of the family Plethodontidae. The name of the salamander from which each photomicrograph has been obtained is given immediately after the figure number.

Recombination requires that the genic material from two different individuals be brought into intimate association by means of nuclear fusion and meiosis. In salamanders, as in all vertebrates, nuclear fusion takes place during the process of fertilization after a sperm has entered an egg. The nucleus of the resulting zygote thus contains two intimately associated sets of Chromosomes from different individual salamanders, one set derived from the sperm, a second from the egg. The Chromosomes of the zygote nucleus, therefore, exist in pairs: for each Chromosome brought in by the sperm nucleus, there will be a "partner" Chromosome from the egg nucleus. In many of the plethodontid salamanders (but not all of them) there are twenty-eight Chromosomes in the zygote nucleus, fourteen brought in by the sperm and fourteen by the egg, resulting in fourteen pairs of "partner" Chromosomes. Since one member of such a pair of Chromosomes is homologous to the other member, the zygote nucleus contains fourteen pairs of homologous Chromosomes.

Through mitosis, the zygote gives rise to the thousands of cells that make up the mature salamander. Recombination of the genic material of the pairs of homologous Chromosomes takes place during meiosis. In salamanders and other vertebrates the two meiotic divisions occur only in the cells that are to become the gametes. In the male, for example, these are the cells of the germinal epithelium of the testis. For a time, these cells divide by mitosis, but, eventually, mitotic division ceases and the cells carry out the two divisions of meiosis, after which they undergo complex morphological changes that transform them into sperm cells.

Figure 7A.1 shows an unfixed and unstained salamander testis cell (spermatocyte) just entering the first meiotic division. It is in a tissue culture chamber, somewhat compressed beneath a strip of dialysis membrane, and has been photographed with phase contrast optics. The large oval nucleus contains an almost centrally located nucleolus. Although the Chromosome strands cannot be seen, the heterochromatic areas associated with the Chromosome centromeres are visible as small dark granules scattered throughout the nucleus. The cytoplasm contains many large dense granules and rodlike mitochondria that are not clearly in focus. The conspicuous spherical structure in the cytoplasm is known as an ideosome. It consists of a central area of clear cytoplasm, surrounded by a layer of compact granules, within which a pair of centrioles (not visible in the photomicrograph) is imbedded. During the first meiotic division, the ideosome divides, giving rise to the poles from which the spindle fibers radiate. This photomicrograph was obtained from a preparation made by Mr. Takeshi Seto and myself in Dr. C. M. Pomerat's tissue culture laboratory at the Pasadena Foundation for Medical Research. It was made during our study of meiosis in living, cultured salamander spermatocytes.

The other photomicrographs were obtained from acetic-orcein squash preparations of salamander spermatocytes, made in connection with my research on the cytoevolution of the plethodontid salamanders. To obtain preparations such as those illustrated in the photomicrographs, one must have spermatocytes from a meiotically active testis. The two meiotic divisions enter the testes of temperate zone salamanders once each year; they may occur in the spring, summer, or fall, depending upon the kind of salamander. A suspension of these spermatocytes is made on a slide and mixed with a drop of the stain-fixative acetic-orcein (2 per cent orcein in 45 per cent acetic acid). A cover glass is placed over the suspension of stained cells, the slide is inverted over several thicknesses of paper towels, and the cells are squashed by pressure on the back of the slide. This squashing separates the Chromosomes and pushes them into a single plane so that their observation under the microscope is greatly simplified. A good grade of orcein will stain only the Chromosomes; cytoplasmic structures, such as those seen in Fig. 7A.1, are not visible in the acetic-orcein squashes. In observing the photomicrographs, remember that the normal arrangement of the Chromosomes within the cell has been disrupted by the squashing.

The Chromosomes first become visible as faintly staining, elongated strands in the leptotene stage of the first meiotic prophase. Chemical studies indicate that DNA duplication occurs sometime prior to leptotene, but the double nature of the genic material is not visible under the microscope at the beginning of the first meiotic prophase. The synapsis of the homologous Chromosomes becomes visible during zygotene, illustrated in Fig. 7A.2 by the large nuclei containing the more lightly staining strands. In many parts of these nuclei it is possible to see that the strands are arranged in pairs, indicating that synapsis is occurring. In zygotene, the elongated strands of leptotene appear to have become shorter and thicker because they are being thrown into more and more compact coils, as can be seen in some of the zygotene nuclei of the photomicrograph. The deeply staining granules conspicuous in these nuclei are heterochromatic areas associated with the Chromosome centromeres, differing from those seen in Fig. 7A.1 in that they are now arranged in pairs.

In Fig. 7.A2, the pachytene stage of the first meiotic prophase is represented by the single large nucleus in which the Chromosomes appear as deeply staining jumbled-up loops. In other organisms, e.g., maize, the Chromosomal duplication that took place prior to leptotene becomes visible at this stage so that the pachytene loops appear as four-strand structures (cf. Fig. 7.1c). But in acetic-orcein squashes of salamander spermatocytes, the individual strands cannot be clearly resolved at pachytene. A typical salamander spermatocyte nucleus at pachytene contains the haploid number of loops with their free ends directed approximately toward the part of the cytoplasm in which the ideosome is located. In salamanders, the preleptotene Chromosomal duplication becomes clearly visible during very early diplotene. Fig. 7A.3 shows a spermatocyte nucleus at this stage, and although the double nature of each strand is not well shown in the photomicrograph, careful focusing on this nucleus reveals the earlier duplication.

In Figs. 7A.4–7 we see with remarkable clarity the four-strand structures that constitute the diplotene stage of the first meiotic prophase, diagrammed in Fig. 7.1d. Although each of these can be called a bivalent, the frequently used term *tetrad* is more descriptive of the four-strand condition. Each strand is known as a chromatid; in Fig. 7A.4, there are 13 tetrads (bivalents), each of which is composed of four chromatids. If you find these terms confusing, simply remember that each Chromosomal structure within the cell at this stage of meiosis consists of four strands of genic material, produced through the duplication of a synapsed pair of homologous Chromosomes. It follows that two of the four strands are homologous to the other two, and having been derived from different individuals, may be genically different. But a strand derived from another by duplication (a sister strand) must be genically identical to the strand from which it is derived, assuming no mistakes in the duplication process. Each Chromosome, then, at diplotene is paired with its homologue and is closely associated with a sister strand.

The component halves of each diplotene tetrad are separated from each other except at points of crossover or chiasma. It is at the chiasmata that breaks and exchanges of the strands appear to occur, thus producing genic recombination. Study the photomicrographs carefully and note that each chiasma involves only two of the four strands. Moreover, the two strands involved are always homologues, never sister strands. Terminalization of the chiasmata does not occur in plethodontid salamanders. The chiasmata seen during early diplotene remain in the tetrad until its dismemberment at the first meiotic anaphase.

The metaphase of the first meiotic division is shown in Figs. 7A.8 and 7A.9. The tetrads move to the equatorial position within the cell; the homologous centromeres have become widely separated, but the arms on either side of the centromeres remain locked in chiasmata. Fig. 7A.8 shows the metaphase tetrads in a side view (somewhat disrupted from their normal equatorial position) ; Fig. 7A.9 shows them in polar view.

The four strands of each tetrad are dismembered by the two meiotic anaphases. The anaphase of the first meiotic division separates the four strands two from two, and the second meiotic anaphase separates the resulting two-strand structures one from one. These events are illustrated in the remaining photomicrographs. The early anaphase of the first meiotic division is shown in Fig. 7A.10. Here one can see that homologous centromeres are moving in opposite directions, bringing about a two-from-two separation of the four strands of each tetrad. Fig. 7A.11 is comparable to Fig. 7.1e, and Fig. 7A.12 illustrates an even later stage of the first meiotic anaphase. The two-strand structures that are obtained by the anaphase of the first meiotic division are called dyads. The two strands of each dyad remain attached to each other by means of material in the heterochromatic regions on either side of their centromeres.

The brief interphase between the first and second meiotic divisions is not illustrated in the photomicrographs. The dyads seen in Fig. 7A.13 are in a late prophase of the second meiotic division (cf. Fig. 7.1f). The metaphase of the second meiotic division is indicated by the movement of the dyads to the equatorial position within the cell, as shown in Fig. 7A.14, in which the normal metaphase position of the dyads has been somewhat shifted by the squashing process. The separation of the two strands of each dyad occurs at the anaphase of the second meiotic division, as shown in Figs. 7A.15 and 7A.16 (cf. Figs. 7.1g and 7.1h). These last two photomicrographs were obtained from a salamander in which the diploid Chromosome number is 26. But there are only 13 Chromosomes in each of the groups shown in Figs. 7A.15 and 7A.16: the meiotic divisions have brought about a halving of the Chromosome number. This occurs because meiosis involves two cellular divisions but only a single Chromosomal duplication. At each of the two divisions half of the strands go into one cell and half into the other;

it is in this way that meiosis produces four cells containing only half the number of chromosomes of the cell from which they have been derived. We should note particularly that the pairs of homologous Chromosomes that existed together in the nucleus of the preleptotene spermatocyte (and that become genically modified by recombination at diplotene) are sharply separated by the two meiotic divisions so that each of the four cellular products of meiosis contains only one member of a particular homologous pair.

The two meiotic divisions are now completed. Let's think back over the various events that have occurred and summarize them. (1) Chemical studies show that a Chromosomal duplication takes place sometime prior to the prophase of the first meiotic division. This doubleness of the Chromosome strands does not become visible until later. (2) Synapsis occurs during zygotene, bringing the homologous strands into an intimate contact. (3) At diplotene the preleptotene Chromosomal duplication becomes visible so that one sees four-strand Chromosomal structures. (4) As diplotene proceeds, the points of crossover of the homologous strands become clearly indicated. These appear to be the places at which breaks and exchanges are taking place; thus, unless appearances are deceiving, it is at this time that recombination of the genic material of homologous strands occurs. (5) The four strands of each diplotene tetrad are dismembered by the two meiotic anaphases. The first anaphase separates the four strands two from two and the second anaphase separates the resulting two-stranded dyads one from one. (6) The four cells that result from the two meiotic divisions contain only half the number of Chromosomes of the cell from which they have been derived, since the two cellular divisions involve only a single Chromosomal duplication. (7) The two members of each homologous pair of Chromosomes, genically modified by recombination, are sharply separated from each other by meiosis and segregated into different nuclei so that each of the four products of a meiosis will have only one member of a given homologous pair. Random nuclear fusions among these haploid cells (the sperms and eggs of salamanders) will restore the diploid chromosome number, bringing the modified pairs of homologues into the intimate association of a single nucleus and making possible still other kinds of genic combinations during the succeeding meiosis.

Fig. 7A.1 (*Batrachoseps wrighti*). A living, cultured spermatocyte, photographed with phase contrast optics.

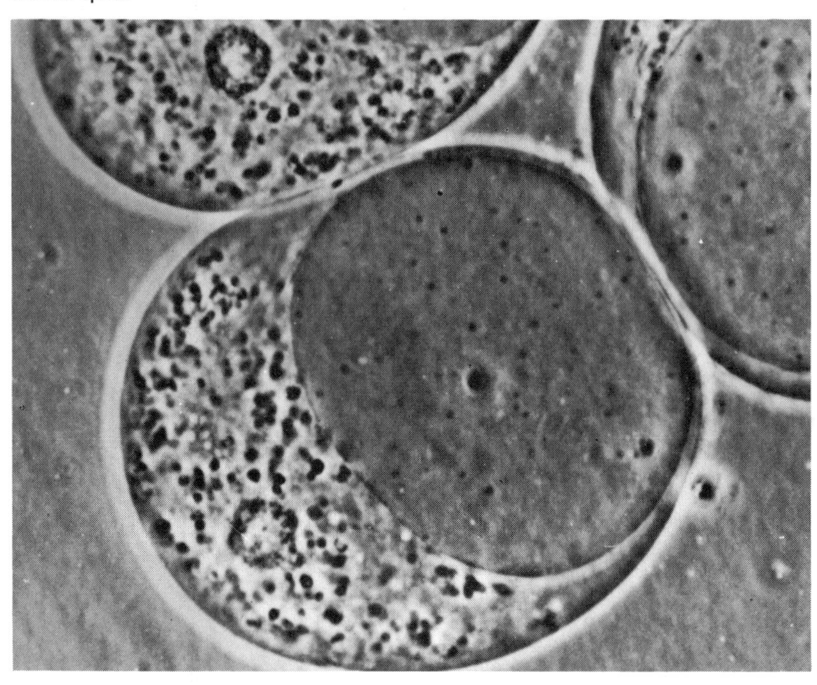

Fig. 7A.2 (*Plethodon vehiculum*). The larger nuclei containing the more lightly staining strands are in the zygotene stage of the first meiotic prophase. The single nucleus in which the strands appear as deeply staining jumbled-up loops is in pachytene. (Cf. Figs. 7.1b and 7.1c.)

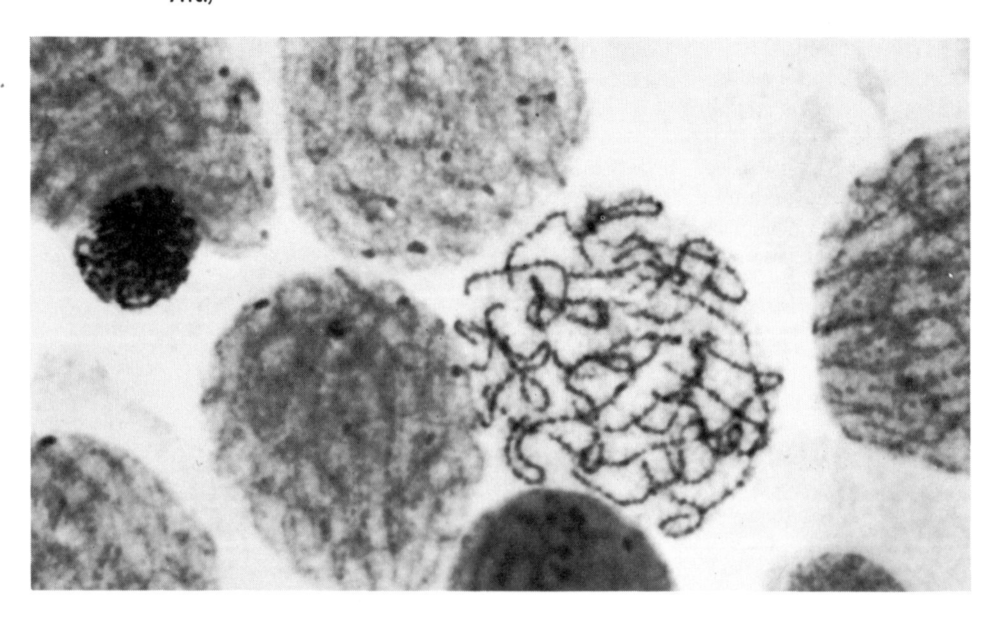

Fig. 7A.3 (*Plethodon vehiculum*). Early diplotene tetrads.

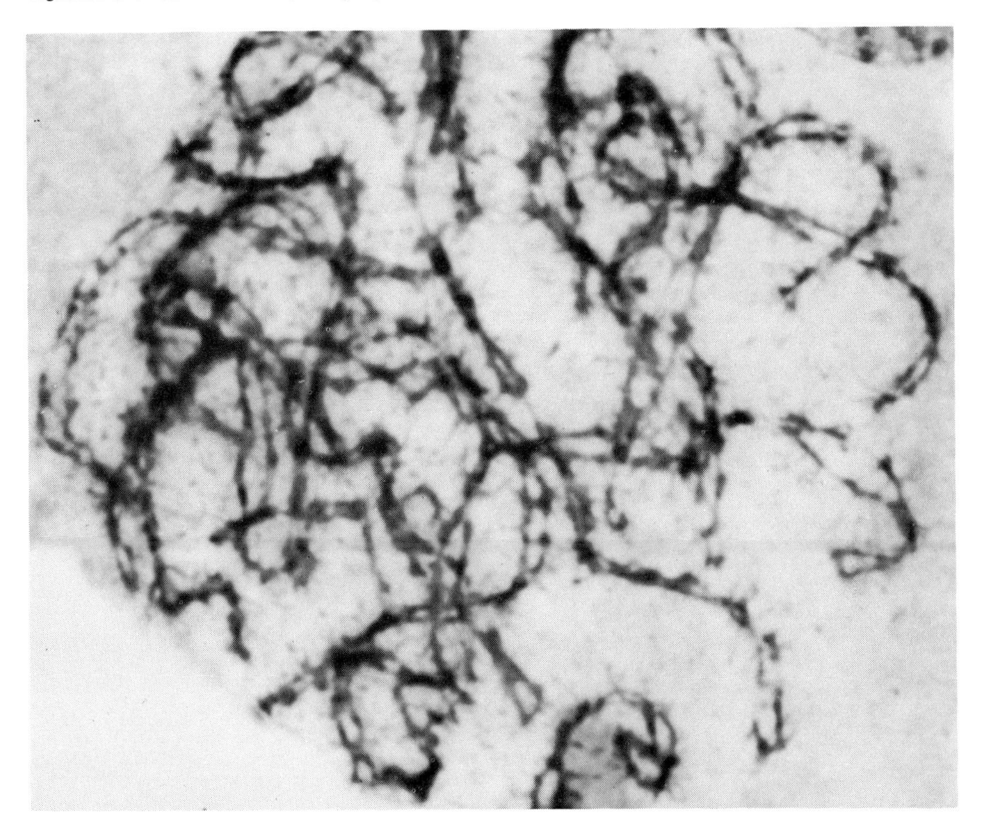

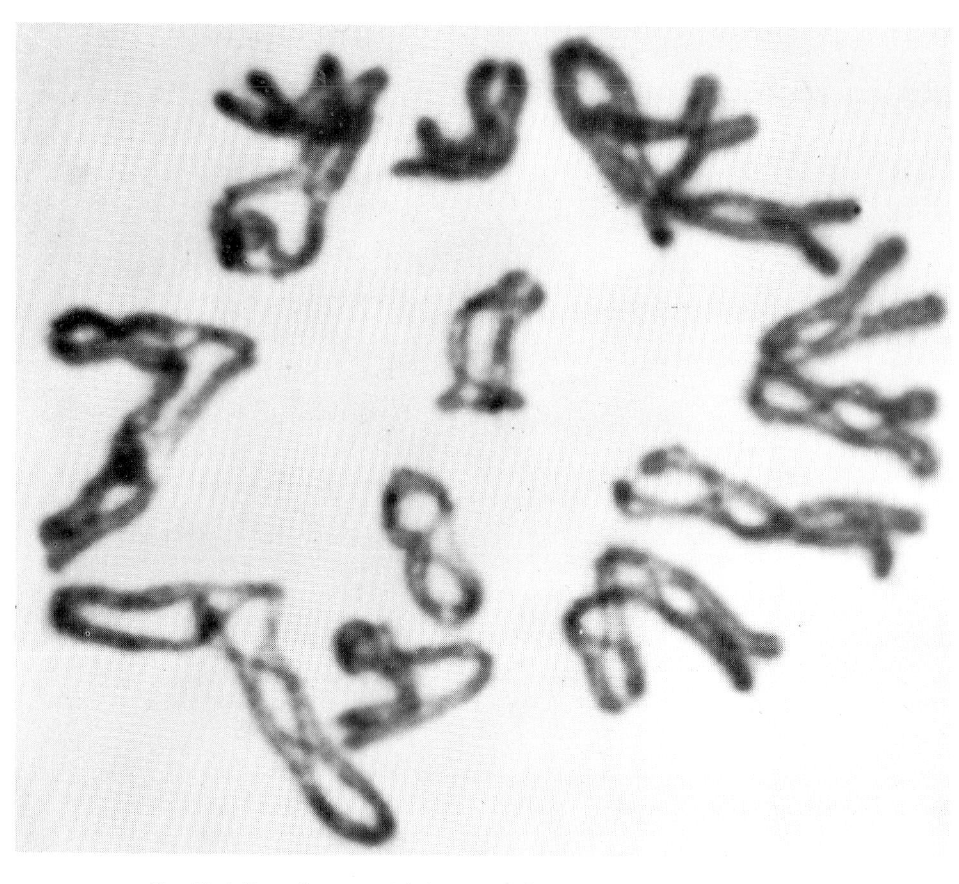

Fig. 7A.4 (*Batrachoseps wrighti*). Late diplotene tetrads. (Cf. Fig. 7.1d.)

Fig. 7A.5 (*Aneides ferreus*). Late diplotene tetrads. (Cf. Fig. 7.1d.)

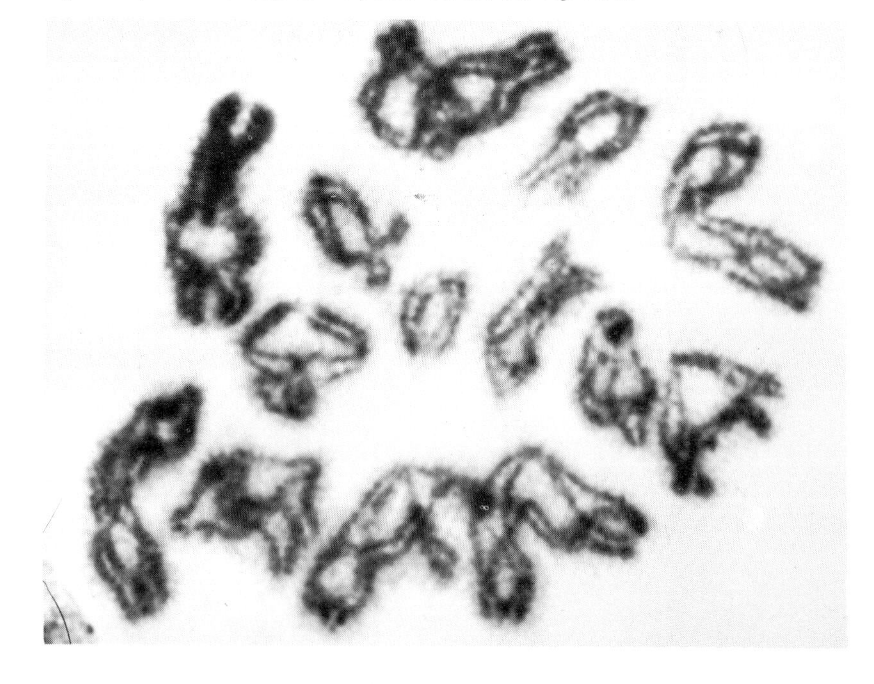

Fig. 7A.6 (*Batrachoseps wrighti*). Two diplotene tetrads in which the four-strand structure is particularly clear. These tetrads are bent at their centromeres, which are centrally located in the tetrad to the right and are near the upper end in the tetrad to the left. In this photomicrograph, it is possible to see that only non-sister-strands are involved in the crossovers. (Cf. Fig. 7.1d.)

Fig. 7A.7 (*Oedipina poelzi*). This late diplotene tetrad, obtained from a recently described Central American plethodontid salamander, is particularly remarkable for the clarity with which the centromeres are shown. Although the structure of the salamander centromere at meiosis is as yet not entirely clear, unpublished observations suggest that at early diplotene each of the four strands has its own separate centromere and that sister centromeres are held together by material in the heterochromatic regions on either side of them. (Cf. Fig. 7.1d.)

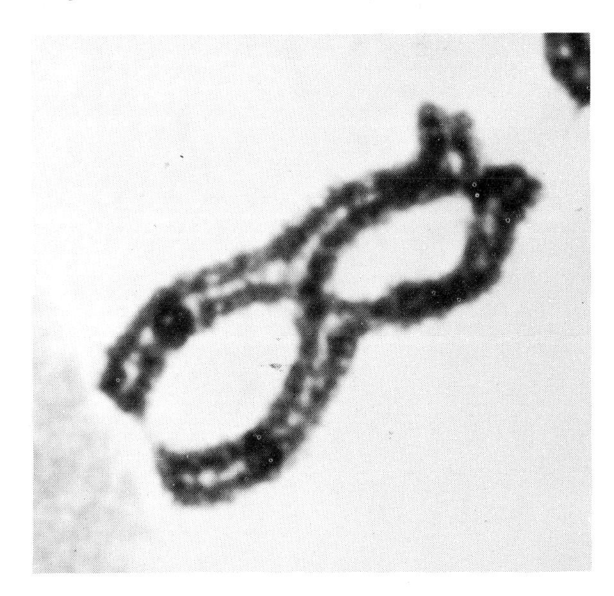

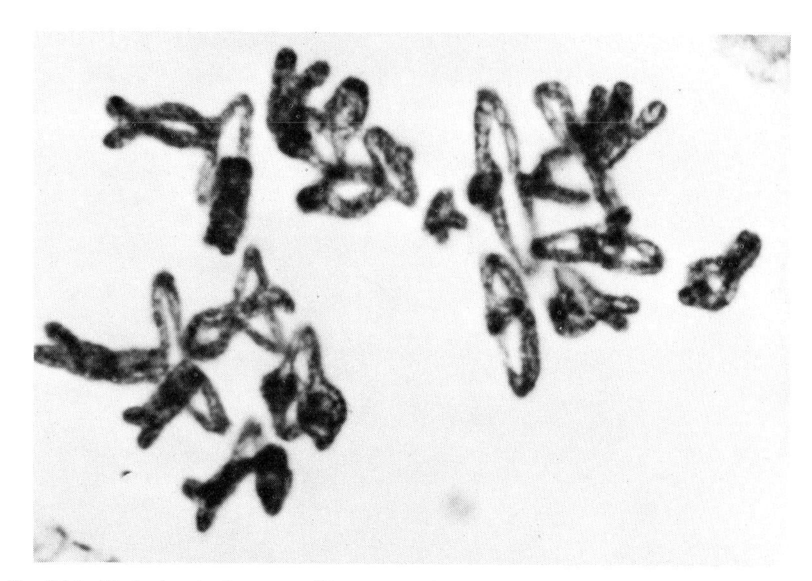

Fig. 7A.8 (*Plethodon jordani metcalfi*). Equatorial view of tetrads at metaphase of the first meiotic division. Homologous centromeres are widely separated; the arms on either side of the centromeres are locked in chiasmata.

Fig. 7A.9 (*Plethodon jordani jordani*). Polar view of first meiotic metaphase tetrads.

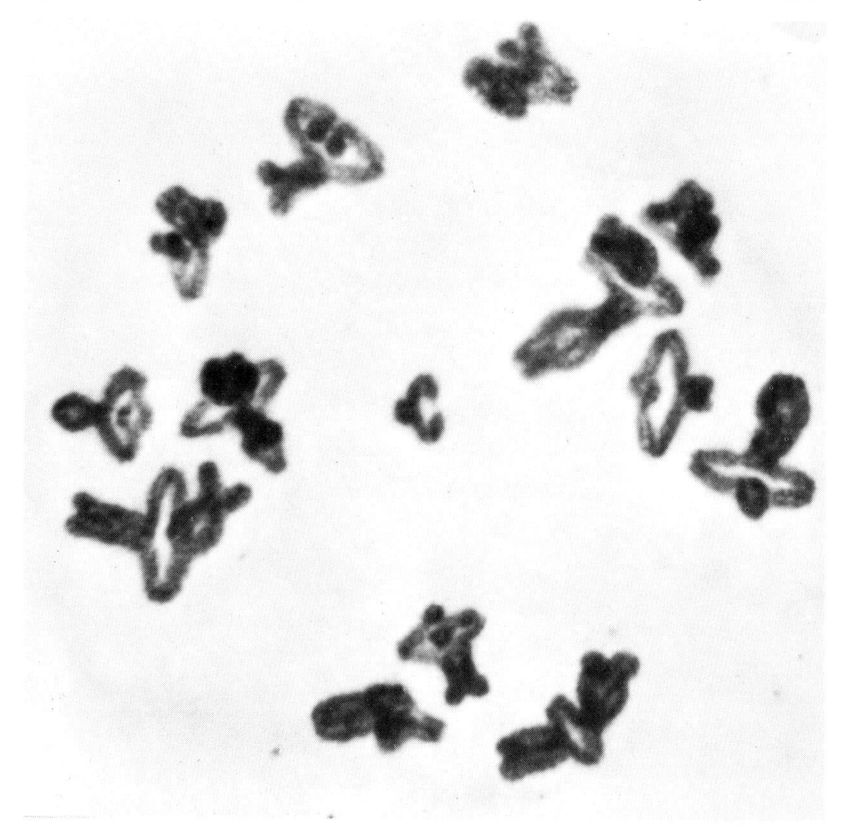

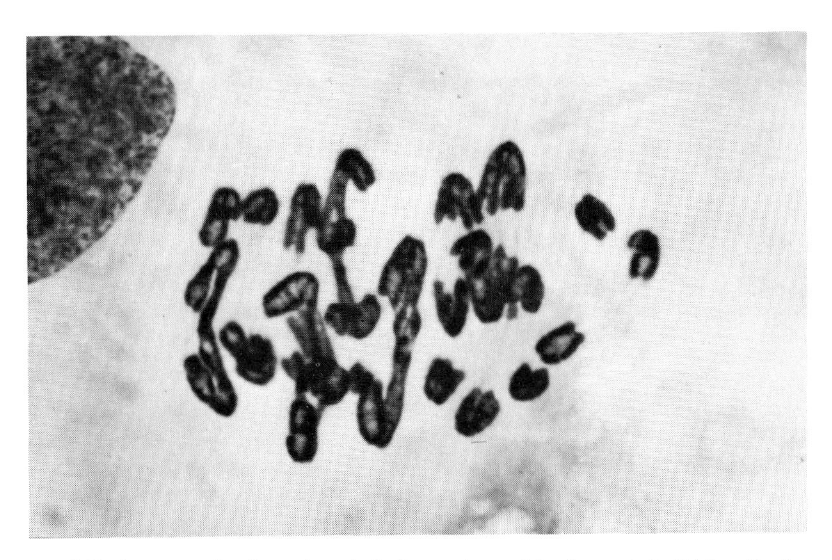

Fig. 7A.10 (*Desmognathus fuscus fuscus*). Early anaphase of the first meiotic division. The four-strand tetrads are undergoing dismemberment into two-strand dyads. As explained in the caption of Fig. 7A.7, the two strands of a dyad are held together by material in the heterochromatic regions on either side of the centromeres.

Fig. 7A.11 (*Bolitoglossa subpalmata*). Later anaphase of the first meiotic division. (Cf. Fig. 7.1e.)

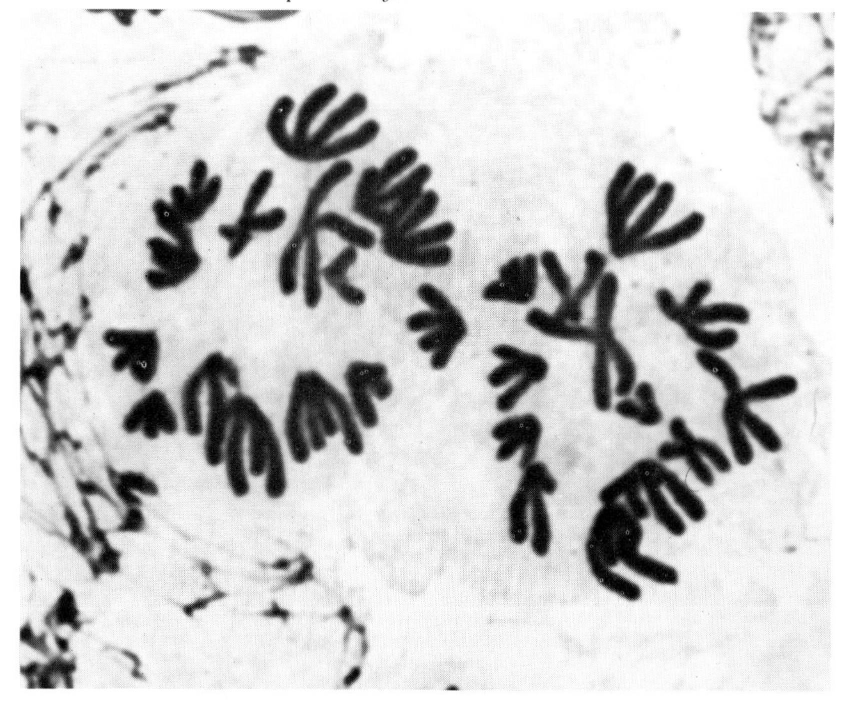

Fig. 7A.12 (*Hydromantes italicus gormani*). Late anaphase of the first meiotic division.

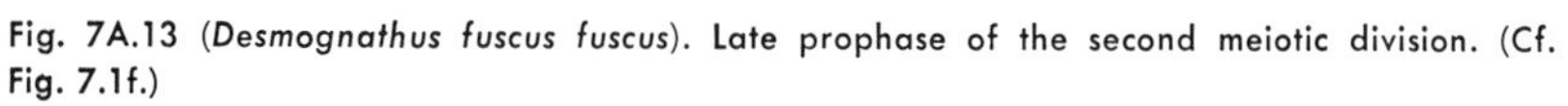

Fig. 7A.13 (*Desmognathus fuscus fuscus*). Late prophase of the second meiotic division. (Cf. Fig. 7.1f.)

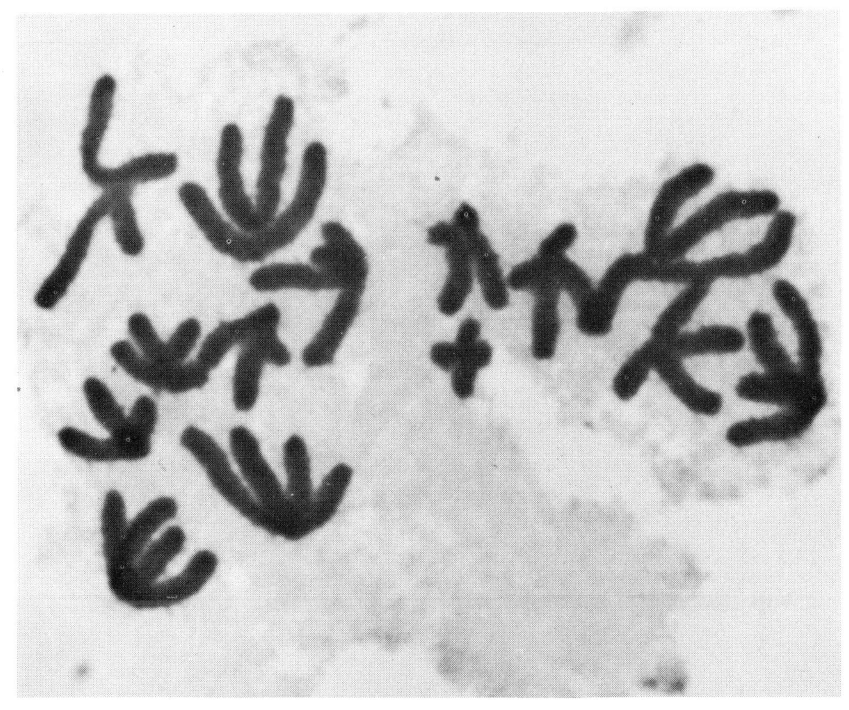

Fig. 7A.14 (*Hydromantes shastae*). Metaphase of the second meiotic division.

Fig. 7A.15 (*Batrachoseps wrighti*). Anaphase of the second meiotic division. (Cf. Fig. 7.1g.)

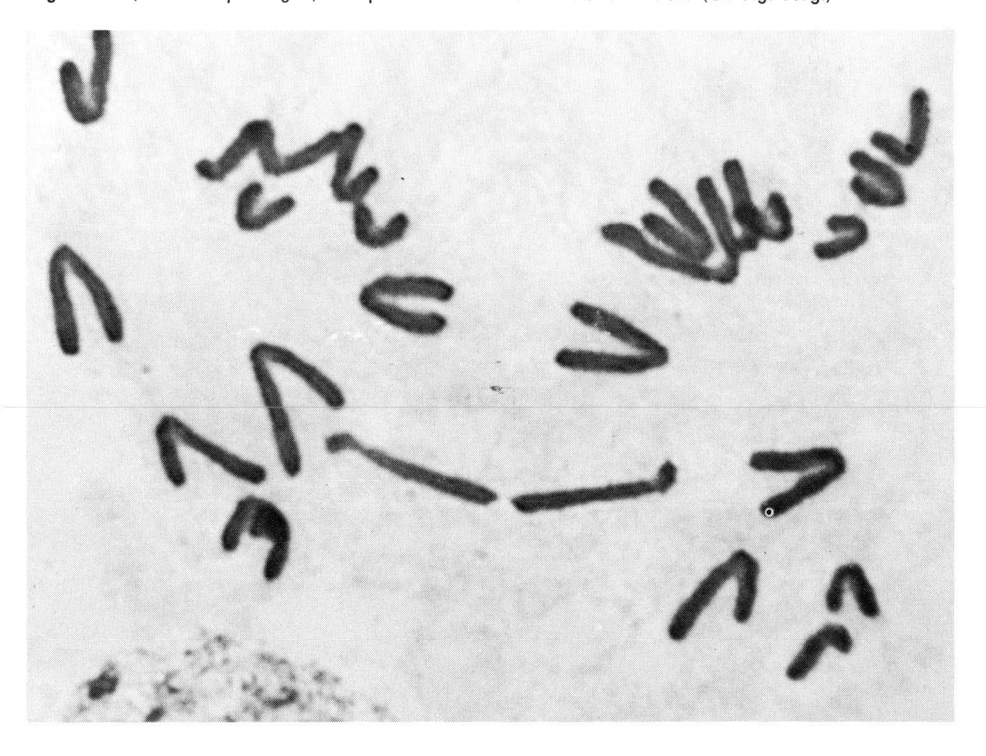

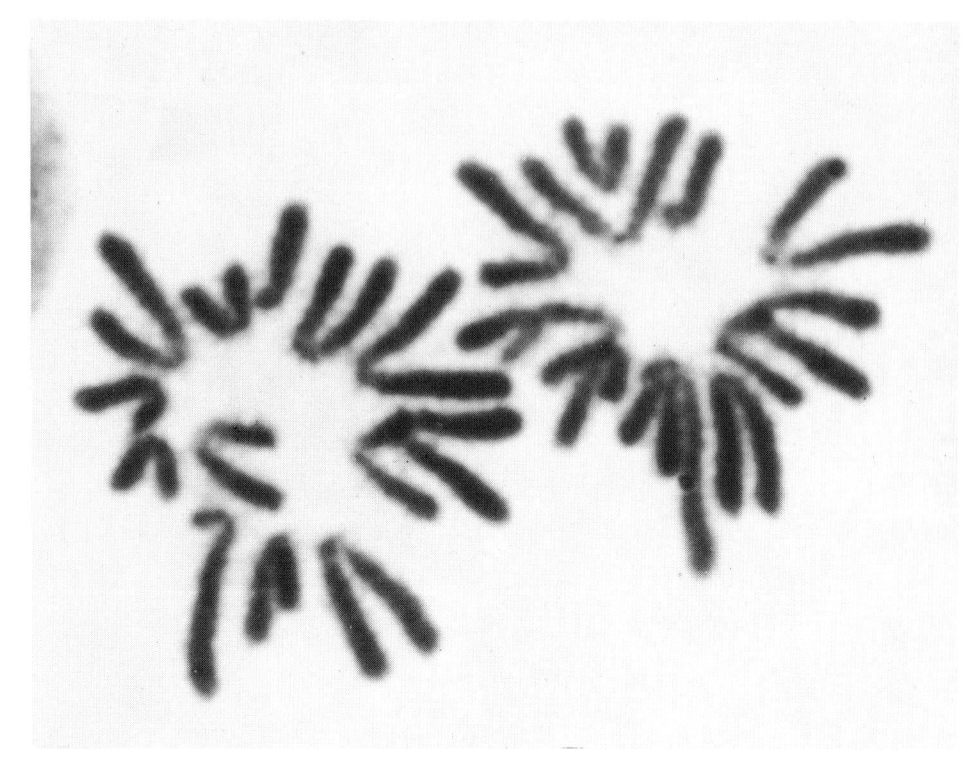

Fig. 7A.16 (*Batrachoseps wrighti.*) Late anaphase of the second meiotic division. The two strands of each dyad have been separated, yielding two haploid Chromosome sets. Each of the two groups of Chromosomes seen here will constitute the genic material of a sperm nucleus. (Cf. Fig. 7.1h.)

Eight

Recombination in Viruses

In the previous chapter, we examined the rules governing recombination in higher organisms. These rules, though they always lead to a reflection in the map of the linear organization of the Chromosome, are different for very closely linked markers and for relatively loosely linked markers. There is a temptation to suppose that Chromosomes are composed of many DNA molecules connected end to end and that two "close" loci are typically resident on the same DNA molecule, whereas "loosely linked loci" are always on different DNA molecules. Two distinct mechanisms of recombination could then be invoked. We would suppose that recombination between distant loci is typically a consequence of the breakage and reunion of the "linkers" connecting adjacent DNA molecules. This process would invariably be reciprocal, and we'd call it "crossing over." Markers at closely linked loci, on the other hand, would recombine by a distinctly different mechanism that permits exchange within the limits of a DNA molecule. This exchange mechanism would typically give nonreciprocal products. Regardless of the degree of validity of this (rather popular) set of notions, the ideas involved do provide us with an introduction to the study of recombination in viruses; the entire chromosome of a virus probably is a single DNA molecule, and we shall see that the rules governing recombination in viruses are in some respects similar to those governing recombination between markers at closely linked loci in higher organisms.

A phage cross

A "cross" in the case of viruses occurs as a consequence of simultaneous infection of a cell by two or more different hereditary types of the same virus. For the bacteriophages, such mixed multiple infections are accomplished in the laboratory as follows: Bacteria (at high concentration, say 10^8 cells per ml., to promote adsorption of phages) are added to a suspension of two phage types, each at a final concentration several times that of the bacterial concentration. For the sake of brevity let's call the two infecting phage types a^+b and ab^+. Four types of phages are observable among the earliest mature particles (see Problem 4.3)—the infecting "parental" types and the recombinant types ab and a^+b^+. Populations of particles maturing in successive intervals contain progressively higher frequencies of recombinants.

Ideas about the mode of the interactions among chromosomes that lead to the production of recombinants fall into two groups. One assumes that the "pool" of DNA from which mature particles are constructed is composed of independently multiplying fragments that undergo repetitive rejoinings and fragmentations at new places. Complete chromosomes, when (if?) they arise can be condensed and matured. This notion may be correct, but as a framework for thought it has not yet been formulated in a useful fashion.

The mating theory

The other group of ideas initially formulated by Nicolo Visconti and Max Delbrück in the early 1950's specifically hypothesizes that fragments of phage chromosomes do not have an independent existence during the recombination and duplication processes within the host cell. In particular, their formulation assumed that *intact* chromosomes "synapse" (mate) in pairs and at random with respect to the markers carried. Exchange, which may or may not involve concomitant duplication of DNA, occurs at a number of spots more or less randomly along the synapsed chromosomes. The precise formulation of Visconti and Delbrück's notions is somewhat more simply arrived at if we assume that the recombination process does not involve concomitant DNA synthesis. The form of the expression is independent of the assumption, and furthermore, recent experiments[1] indicate that

[1] The synthesis of phage DNA in infected bacterial cells can be blocked in several ways. Two methods of stopping DNA synthesis by preventing thymine synthesis have been exploited. For the phage λ, infection of thymine-auxotroph host cells in the absence of supplied thymine provides the appropriate conditions. The "T-even" phages, T2, T4, and T6, however, direct the synthesis of thymine-producing enzymes themselves, so that in the absence of the appropriate mutant phage strains the same experiment cannot be performed. However, the structural analogue of thymidine, 5-fluorodeoxy-uridine, interacts with both the host-cell enzymes and the phage-produced enzymes for thymidine synthesis in such a way as to prevent their function.

recombination can proceed more or less normally in the absence of DNA synthesis.

The relationship between the frequency of recombinants in the mating pool and the average number of exchanges (map distance/100) between two loci per mating can be arrived at by simple considerations. For expository convenience we can approach the problem by first establishing a relation between frequency of recombinants in the mating pool and the recombinant frequency resulting from a single round of matings between chromosomes of complementary parental type.

Let's first define some symbols. Let

p, as usual, equal the frequency of recombinants from matings between chromosomes of complementary parental type.

f equal the frequency in the mating pool of chromosomes carrying, say, the allele a. This in turn equals the frequency among the infecting phage of the type ab^+.

Now, close your eyes and grab a chromosome from the pool, please. Your chromosome inherited its nucleotide sequence at, say, the a locus from *one* of the infecting particles. We now define a line of descent (lineage) by inheritance of sequence at the a locus. Thus, with a probability f, your chromosome is type a.

Let m equal the average number of matings per lineage.

Then, mp equals the average number of occurrences per lineage of an exchange pattern that could lead to recombination for loci a and b.

If matings are Poisson distributed among lineages, then $(1 - e^{-mp})$ equals the probability that a lineage has had at least one mating with an exchange pattern that could recombine markers.

The chance that your chromosome is type ab depends on the chance that the *last* such mating in its lineage was with a particle carrying the marker b. This chance is simply $(1 - f)$. Therefore, your chromosome is of type ab with a probability of $f(1 - f)(1 - e^{-mp})$. A symmetric argument applies for the recombinant type a^+b^+, so that the average frequency of recombinants in the pool is given by

$$R = 2f(1 - f)(1 - e^{-mp}) \qquad \text{(Eq. 8.1)}$$

R cannot generally be measured directly, since for some phages the "naked" chromosomes are not demonstrably infective and for others the chromosomes are infective only with a very low efficiency. R can be related, however, to the frequency of recombinants among mature phages as they accumulate in the infected cells. The usual assumptions are that the phages maturing at any instant represent a random sample of the pool at that instant[2] and that mating and maturation both proceed at a constant rate. The mature phages, then, represent an average of the pool situation that can be represented by

[2] This assumption is probably somewhat in error since it does not take into account the existence of the several noninfectious stages in maturation that are known to exist.

averaging the expression for R between two values of m. The m values to be chosen are m_1, the average mating experience of the first maturing chromosomes, and m_2, the average mating experience of the last. The appropriate expression (obtainable by integration) is

$$\overline{R} = 2f(1-f)\left[1 + \frac{e^{-m_2p} - e^{-m_1p}}{(m_2 - m_1)p}\right] \qquad \text{(Eq. 8.2)}$$

One more factor must be taken into account in the relationship between R and p. In a typical experiment the two infecting types are each Poisson distributed upon the host cells so that not every cell is characterized by the same f value. This variation in f has been algebraically estimated to reduce the observed frequencies of recombinants by about 10 per cent when the total average number of phage particles absorbed per cell is 14 (a number conventionally adopted by those who perform phage crosses). Therefore a complete expression for $\overline{R}$ is more precisely given by

$$\overline{R} = 2(0.9)f(1-f)\left[1 + \frac{e^{-m_2p} - e^{-m_1p}}{(m_2 - m_1)p}\right] \qquad \text{(Eq. 8.3)}$$ [3]

Whenever it's not misleading, let's relate our arguments to the more appealing expression 8.1; the primary assumptions are embodied in it, and they're not obscured by the "complications" embodied in 8.3.

The value of f can be systematically varied by adjusting the relative amounts of the two infecting types of phages. R is observed to be proportional to $f(1-f)$. If we assume that m, the average number of matings per lineage, is proportional to time, we can test the appropriateness of the factor $(1 - e^{-mp})$. For loci close together on the map, p is small, and, therefore, mp is small so that R increases linearly in time. For markers distant on the map, if m becomes sufficiently large, R asymptotically approaches the value $f(1-f)$. These features of the formulation have been tested and passed for several phages. Since the Visconti–Delbrück idea does provide a rational framework within which to proceed, we shall use it. However, remind yourself occasionally that the model, though useful, is possibly oversimplified.

The linear mapping function

The three unrelated phages, λ, T1, and T4, have been mapped with unusual thoroughness. We must first consider in detail the results of crosses with λ and T1. We can write a null hypothesis relating

[3] The estimate of the coefficient 0.9 assumes that all the particles that adsorb to a bacterium can duplicate and that they and their descendants can, with equal probability, participate in recombination with particles of the other genotype. The degree to which these assumptions are justifiable will be indicated later.

p with the average number of exchanges per mating, d, by analogy with higher organisms:[4]

$$p = \tfrac{1}{2}(1 - e^{-2d})$$

Combining this expression with Eq. 8.1 we get

$$R = 2f(1 - f)\left\{1 - \exp\left[\frac{-m}{2}(1 - e^{-2d})\right]\right\} \qquad \text{(Eq. 8.4)}$$

A "standard" cross is performed with equal input of the two parental types so that $f = \frac{1}{2}$ and

$$R = \frac{1}{2}\left\{1 - \exp\left[\frac{-m}{2}(1 - e^{-2d})\right]\right\} \qquad \text{(Eq. 8.5)}$$

Let's examine the properties of this expression in order to seek means of testing its adequacy as a mapping function for λ and T1. In Fig. 8.1a, R is plotted as a function of d for several values of m; in Fig. 8.1b, R is plotted as a function of m for several values of d.

For any species of phage whose mating regime is characterized by a particular value of m, we see that with increasing d, R reaches a maximum value determined by the m value. This relation suggests a method for estimating m for a phage species. For phage λ, markers distant on the map give R values in the neighborhood of 0.13. Markers somewhat more distant on the map give about the same values. Therefore, it looks as though m equals about 0.6 for λ. All in all, the mapping function plotted in Fig. 8.1a evaluated at m equal to 0.6 seems to convert R values for λ to additive d values adequately. (We shall explore corollary features of Fig. 8.1 in Problem 8.2.) The mapping function, evaluated at $m = 1$, works for T1 as well.

Although the linear mapping function does seem to "work," the model upon which it is based ought not to be taken too seriously. Different sets of assumptions can give equally "good" functions, and

[4] This relationship between recombinant frequency and "distance" may be derived without reference to higher organisms. It is quite possible that crossing over in phage does not procede in a four-stranded bivalent. If a phage mating involves simply a pairing between just two DNA molecules followed by crossing over without an intervening act of duplication, then markers at two loci would recombine whenever an odd number of crossovers occurred between them. Let y be the average number of crossovers between a particular pair of loci. If the crossovers were Poisson distributed among the synapsed chromosome "pairs," then p would equal the sum of the odd terms of the Poisson distribution of mean y.

$$p = ye^{-y} + \frac{y^3e^{-y}}{3!} + \frac{y^5e^{-y}}{5!} + \cdots$$

I leave it to my algebraically inclined students to demonstrate that this can be simplified to

$$p = \tfrac{1}{2}(1 - e^{-2y})$$

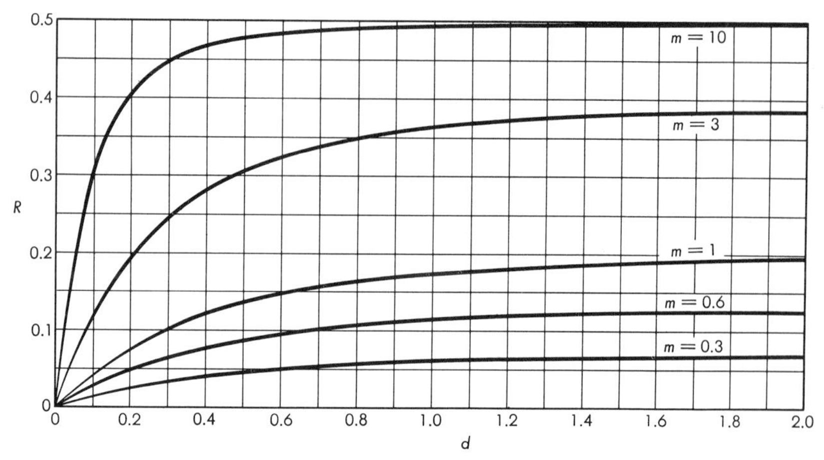

Fig. 8.1a. The mapping function (Eq. 8.5) for phages with a linear map plotted for several values of *m*, the number of rounds of mating per particle.

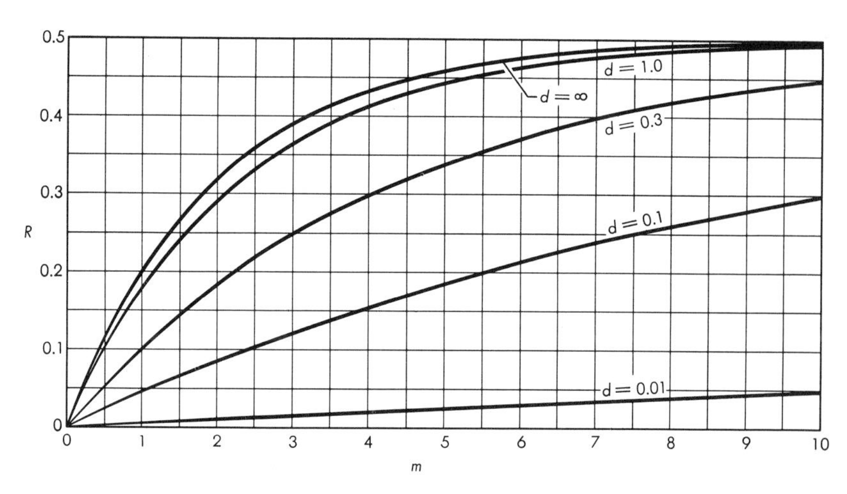

8.1b. The dependence of phage recombinant frequencies *R* on rounds of mating *m* for various map distances *d* (Eq. 8.5). The frequency of recombinants for closely linked loci increases linearly over a wide range of *m* values. The frequency of recombinants for loosely linked loci rapidly approaches the equilibrium value of 0.5.

there are several reasons to prefer some of these. There are at least two *experimental* reasons for doubting our linear mapping function. (1) For the phage λ it appears that no more than seven of the infecting particles *can* duplicate in a single infected cell. (2) Electron-microscopic observations of infected cells suggest that the clones of chromosomes initiated within a given host cell by the infecting particles do not become well mixed with each other. There is an *emotional* objection as well to our linear mapping function. A chromosome of λ is about 10 times as long as the host cell in which it duplicates (and recombines). Furthermore, the mating pool contains on the order of 100 such sinuous monsters. It is not easy to imagine that two chromosomes in such a spaghetti bowl could synapse and recombine with each other at more than one place at a time. The implication of the first two objections is that heterogeneities exist in the population that were not taken into account by the mapping function as we have written it. The last objection implies positive interference in single mating acts; i.e., each mating may involve one and only one exchange. It is quite possible that these two kinds of nonrandomness could conspire to leave us with data that fit well with the naïvely motivated linear mapping function.

Correspondence between map and chromosome

The relationship between the genetic map of λ and the chromosome of λ was established in the early 1960's by experiments from the laboratories of M. S. Meselson and J. J. Weigle and Dale Kaiser and David Hogness. Since Meselson and Weigle's experiments have especially relevant overtones, let's look at Kaiser and Hogness' experiments first.

An isolated chromosome of λ can (with rather low efficiency) enter a bacterium and multiply in the presence of co-infecting intact λ. The success of such infections is signaled by the appearance among the progeny phages of genetic markers distinguishing the isolated chromosomes. One of the first rewards of the careful development of this experimental system is derived from its application to the study of "half-chromosomes." When a DNA solution is stirred, the DNA molecules are fragmented. Since the shear forces generated by stirring are maximal near the middle of a molecule and are positively correlated with the length of a molecule, stirring at controlled speeds can produce a population of fragments all of which have approximately equal molecular weight; the break in each chromosome occurs near the middle. When these half-chromosomes infect bacterial cells along with intact phages, progeny phages appear that carry markers from the half-chromosomes. When the phage yield from individual cells is examined, it can be seen that a given half-chromosome contributes markers from *half* of the genetic map. At this first glance, then, map distances seem to bear a pleasant relationship to physical distances. Perhaps the experiment has been done with quarter-chromosomes by now.

The experiments of Meselson and Weigle show an equally pleasant correspondence between map distance and physical dimensions of the λ chromosome. Meselson and Weigle infected cells with λ particles carrying genetic markers at two loci located like this on the map: x x. They co-infected with λ heavily substituted with N^{15} and C^{13}. Progeny particles were scored both with respect to their genetic markers (their genotype) and the amount of inherited isotope. Most of the particles of each of the four genotypes contain only DNA synthesized completely *de novo* from the light isotopes of the bacterial culture medium. A small fraction of the particles of each genotype assume positions in an equilibrium density gradient that reflects inheritance of DNA from the isotopically labeled infecting particles. The density distribution of each of the genotypes is depicted in Fig. 8.2.

Detailed interpretations of the distribution of labeled DNA among individuals of each of the four genotypes are still being evolved with the aid of additional experiments; we'll confine our attention here to the relevant features of the distributions.

(1) In addition to the density mode corresponding to completely unlabeled particles, two other modes for the labeled parental genotype are apparent. One of these (drop 17 in Fig. 8.2) reflects the occurrence of progeny phages that have inherited a complete, labeled DNA molecule.[5] The second mode (drop 26) reflects particles that have inherited a semiconservatively replicated chromosome.

(2) The recombinant type (+*mi*) that has inherited the "left-hand" marker on the map of the labeled parent also shows two density modes reflecting substantial inheritance of labeled DNA. The more dense mode (drop 18) signals the inheritance of a chromosome labeled in about 90 per cent of its nucleotides. The chromosomes in such particles must be labeled over most of their length in both chains. The less dense mode (drop 27) signals the inheritance of a chromosome labeled in about 45 per cent of its nucleotides. The two density modes probably result from particles containing chromosomes with label distributions like this

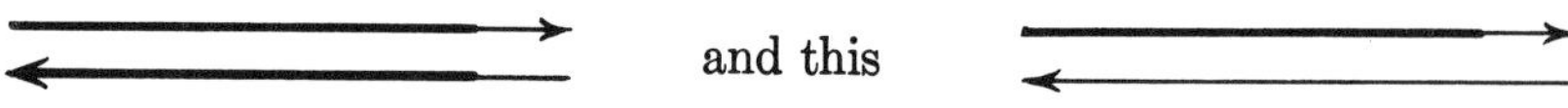

respectively.

For the moment let's be content with drawing the obvious conclusion that recombination can result from the transverse breakage of an unduplicated chromosome.

(3) The recombinant type (*c*+) that has inherited the "right-hand" marker of the labeled parent has a density distribution indicating that the inheritance of that marker from the labeled parent does not involve a conspicuous inheritance of labeled DNA.

The density distributions reveal that the two recombinant genotypes share unequally in the inheritance of labeled DNA. The asymmetry in isotope inheritance correlates well with the asymmetric distribution of the two markers on the map.

The idea of the colinearity of the map and the chromosome of a creature does not represent a new idea in the development of this introduction to the physical basis of inheritance. It was raised here partly to provide a background by contrast to analogous studies among the T-even phages.

[5] These progeny could conceivably be derived from DNA that has duplicated only conservatively. It seems more likely, however, that these fully labeled chromosomes never did duplicate under the experimental conditions of multiple infection.

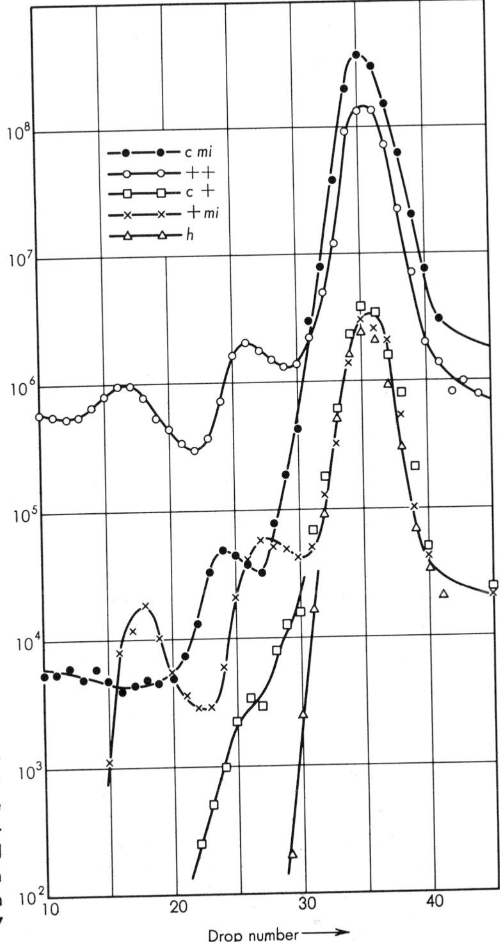

Fig. 8.2. The transmission of labeled DNA into progeny particles from a genetic cross. Wild type λ(++) heavily labeled with N^{15} and C^{13} was crossed with doubly mutant λ(*c mi*) containing the ordinary isotopes C^{12} and N^{14}. The host cells were grown in ordinary medium. The progeny particles were centrifuged to equilibrium in a CsCl density gradient. Successive drops collected after puncturing the bottom of the centrifuge tube were assayed for the titer of each of the four phage genotypes. λ*h* particles were present in the centrifuge tube to provide a density and band-shape reference. The significance of the distributions is discussed on the opposite page. This figure, reproduced by permission of M. S. Meselson and J. J. Weigle, appeared in *Proc. Nat. Acad. Sci. U.S.*, 47 (1961), 863.

Circular maps

The sequence of hundreds of marked loci on the map of T4 has been determined from examinations of recombinant frequencies arising in crosses. The map is linear, unbranched, and of finite length, but it has no ends! It is "circular." The first crosses that clearly established this map configuration involved co-infection by particles marked at three loci (i.e., three-factor crosses). In phages, as in any other creatures, the map sequence of three linked loci is usually more convincingly established by an examination of recombinant frequencies from a single three-factor cross than by comparison of the recombinant frequencies from each of the three possible two-factor crosses involving the same loci. (Should this contention not be obvious, an examination of your answers to Problem 8.2 will convince you.)

When the sequence of three loci, say *a*, *b*, and *h*, was determined, it was found that they were linked in that order. When loci *h*, *i*, and *q* were marked in a three-factor cross, the order was again "alphabetical." (Please don't be confused by my after-the-fact alphabetical renaming of the loci that were actually employed. It will simplify the later parts of this discussion.) Crosses to determine the sequence of loci *q*, *r*, and *y* gave the result you've come to expect. When loci *y*, *z*, and *a* were marked, however, the sequence was clearly seen to be *y–z–a*, with locus *a* tightly linked to *z*. These results can be represented on only one kind of map, a closed curve, or "circular" one.

Several models for the origin of the circular map of T4 seem reasonable at present. Problem 8.3 inquires into the quantitative properties of one of these.

One model supposes that the linear chromosome of each infecting particle assumes a "circular" configuration following injection into a bacterial cell. The second supposes that in each mating act the number of exchanges indulged in is always even. (Convince yourself that this restriction leads to a circular map. Now convince yourself that the same restriction must be imposed upon the first model as well in order to avoid an unpleasant mess.) The third model supposes that among mature phage particles many sequences of loci are represented. Some particles have loci arranged in the order *a–z*, others have sequences *m–za–1*, etc. From what we know of DNA structure and of the map of T4, there is no reason to doubt that this model can entertain as many possible sequences as there are nucleotide pairs in the T4 chromosome (about 2×10^5). Each of these sequences is related to the others by a simple rule: each can be derived by making one "cut" in a hypothetical circular chromosome.

For each of the three models there are a priori reasons for approval. The principal attraction of the supposition of a "circular" chromosome is its obviousness. The second model is seductive because of its potential harmony with an observation of general importance in genetics. Fragments of DNA molecules introduced into cells undergo recombination with the recipient cells without resulting in detectable lethality. In previous chapters we have encountered two instances (transformation and interrupted bacterial conjugation) of recombination occurring between whole chromosomes and parts of chromosomes. These and analogous processes that we shall encounter in Chapter 9 show no biological evidence (lethality) of the fracturing of the recipient chromosome into two parts. Lethality could well be expected as a result of an *odd* number of exchanges between a chromosome and a chromosomal fragment. This negative observation suggests that mechanisms insuring even numbers of exchanges may be naturally selected as a result of the hazards involved in interactions between whole chromosomes and parts of chromosomes. The third model is attractive because of the very close analogy to it in the sexual process of *Escherichia coli* (see Chapter 9). Experiments designed to elucidate the basis of the circular T4 map have all pointed toward the third model. We shall return to this model later in the chapter.

High negative interference and "heterozygotes"

In λ, particles emerging from a cross show a positive correlation in the occurrence of recombination in adjacent regions of the map. This "negative interference" presumably arises from inequalities in the mating experience of the various lineages. Indeed, the primary test of the mapping function we wrote for λ was its ability to convert R values to p values that don't show negative interference. The T4 map also appears to show negative interference, which is probably in part of analogous origin. The analysis of this negative interference is obscured by at least three complications. (1) It's not clear what the definition of interference for a circular map should be. (2) We aren't confident yet of the most reasonable hypothesis for relating R and d. (3) There is clearly negative interference that cannot be attributed to inequalities in mating experience among lineages. This high negative interference becomes stronger for tightly linked markers. (See the footnote to Problem 8.2 for a quantitative definition of high negative interference.) It seems reasonable that the negative interference observed at short distances in higher organisms should be equated either with the negative interference observed at long distance in phages or with the high negative interference that is seen at short distances, but it is not clear which (both?).[6]

In addition to negative interference, recombination results among phages bear at least two other apparent similarities with that for close loci in higher organisms. (1) When phage yields from individual cells are examined, there is no significant correlation in the frequencies of complementary recombinant types; it appears as though a given elementary mating act doesn't produce reciprocal recombinants. (2) Some of the particles emerging from a cross give rise to progeny particles of two different genotypes; these particles carry two allelic markers. (I think this is the first time I've had to abuse our definition of *allele*.) The analysis of these "heterozygotes"[7] is a current activity of phage genetics. The best guess regarding the molecular basis of some of these "heterozygotes" is that they have a structure similar to that of the heteroduplexes arising during mutagenesis (Chapter 5). One chain of the DNA has a nucleotide sequence corresponding to one allele, whereas the other chain has a sequence corresponding to the other. In three-factor crosses, "heterozygotes" for the "middle" marker are typically recombinant for outside markers. This observation suggests that the product of a mating act has a structure like the second one of those shown on page 65 (Chapter 6). Such structures might exist among mature phage particles or they might be only transient intermediates in the formation of recombinants, the gaps in

[6] Since this section was set in type, high negative interference has been detected in phage λ as well.

[7] We'll keep *heterozygotes* in quotes in this chapter because we are somewhat distorting its original definition, which is presented in Chapter 10.

them being "healed" by replication prior to condensation of the chromosome.

Observations in tetrad analysis among higher organisms suggest the existence of similar "heterozygous" chromosomes. Rarely, one of the four meiotic products in crosses between individuals mutant at closely linked loci is observed to give rise in its first postmeiotic mitosis to one wild-type cell and one mutant cell.

In T4 an *additional* molecular basis for "heterozygosity" seems likely. This recent discovery has cast doubt upon certain interpretations of some of the earlier work on "heterozygosity." Furthermore, this second class has as yet given us no better insight into the molecular mechanisms involved in an exchange act than did the first. However, it does provide a valuable clue to the molecular basis of genetic circularity in T4.

In the yield from mixed infections by r and r^+ (wild type), about 1 per cent of the progeny particles are demonstrably "heterozygous" (i.e., give rise to both r and r^+ particles when they infect a bacterium). More systematic measurements of the "heterozygote" frequency have shown that for any r mutant differing from wild type by a minimal difference (presumably a single nucleotide pair), 1.4 per cent of the particles from cells infected by equal numbers of r and r^+ phage are "heterozygous." When the r mutant is a deletion (see Chapter 5 and below), only 0.4 per cent of the offspring of a mixed infection are "heterozygous." This value is independent of the extent of the deletion over a wide range. This result and others, coupled with a handful of preconceptions, suggest that there are two kinds of "heterozygotes"; "small" mutants can indulge in the formation of both kinds, but grosser mutants can participate in the formation of only one. In the early 1960's George Streisinger reasoned this and other observations into a promising hypothesis: only small mutants can form heteroduplex "heterozygotes"; presumably the degree to which the Watson–Crick base-pair requirements can be violated is limited. Deletion mutants, as well as small mutants, can form a second type of "heterozygote." Streisinger's hypothesis explains the second type of "heterozygotes" by supposing that each chromosome in a circularly permuted population possesses a terminal redundancy of the initial loci. A chromosome whose basic sequence is a–z, for example, is more exactly written as a–za^+ if recombination occurred between the terminal loci. The chromosome of such an individual would look like this:

$$\xrightarrow{\hspace{4cm}}$$
$$a \qquad\qquad\qquad\qquad za^+$$
$$\xleftarrow{\hspace{4cm}}$$

where the arrows, as usual, represent the two complementary chains of a DNA molecule. This idea provides an explanation for the origin from a single particle of the proposed circularly permuted population.

Streisinger's notion is that daughter chromosomes in an infected cell can synapse with each other like this:

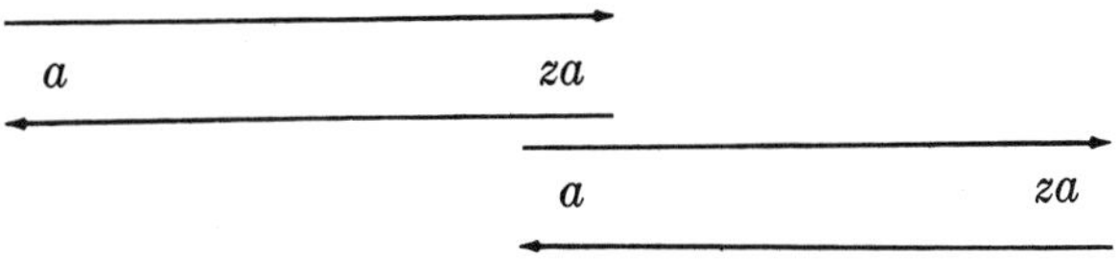

a *za*

a *za*

Exchange in the synapsed region can result in the formation of a "Siamese" chromosome. Reiterations of this process could lead to polymers of the polymer. Sometime before or during maturation, phage-sized chromosomes must be cut out of these monsters. The amount cut out would be a genome-plus-a-bit with starting points in the locus sequence well scrambled. (Could any of the intramolecular "heterozygosity" in higher organisms be of this variety?)

The ideas of polymers of polymers and of circular permutation of nucleotide sequence have both been supported by physical analysis. It is more constructive for our present purposes, however, to consider genetic evidence. A pair of one-factor crosses have been performed that confirm a very special prediction of Streisinger's idea.

Since about two-thirds of the "heterozygotes" for a small mutant are supposed to be heteroduplexes, small-mutant "heterozygotes" should on the whole have a behavior that reflects the semiconservative duplication of DNA. In a pool of multiplying DNA the exchange mechanism that forms them should eventually be balanced by duplication that causes them to segregate. We have seen previously that recombination proceeds essentially normally in the absence of DNA duplication. Under conditions of interrupted DNA synthesis, then, the frequency of heteroduplex "heterozygotes" should increase beyond the equilibrium value usually observed. The frequency of small-mutant "heterozygotes" was observed to rise to values close to 10 per cent when DNA synthesis was blocked by 5-fluorodeoxyuridine. When the inhibition was removed, the frequency of "heterozygotes" rapidly declined toward normal values.

The "heterozygotes" arising in a mixed infection by deletion mutants and wild-type particles should not be subject to segregation by replication (why?). On the other hand, their frequency in the mating pool should reach equilibrium as a consequence of repeated matings. In those chromosomes redundant for the *r* region, the two *r* loci are about as loosely linked as loci can be. Since T4 appears to undergo a large number of matings per lineage (see Problem 8.3), the frequency of deletion "heterozygotes" should approach its equilibrium value (0.4 per cent) early in the course of infection. Furthermore, since recombination proceeds in the presence of 5-fluorodeoxyuridine, the attainment of equilibrium should not be influenced by the presence of the analogue. It isn't.

I'm sure I've conveyed the impression that our understanding of the molecular details of recombination processes is primitive (Watson and Crick left us to find our own way). I hope I've also succeeded in suggesting that a deeper understanding is up for grabs. (Who will be the first to develop an in vitro system for producing recombinants?) In any case, these are the principal phenomena to be explained for phages:

(1) Maps are "linear" for some phages and "circular" for others.

(2) Reciprocal recombinants apparently fail to arise in a correlated fashion in a given infected cell.

(3) An exchange event can be associated with both "heterozygosity" and high negative interference.

Fine-structure analysis

Despite our ignorance of the exchange mechanism in phages (or elsewhere), the use of crosses as an analytical tool has (in phages as elsewhere) been valuable. Seymour Benzer led the way into the area of fine-structure recombination analysis in phages. Hundreds of the thousands of *rII* mutants isolated have been mapped. They all fall within a single sector of the T4 "circle," which comprises not more than a few per cent of the total circumference. The analysis of the *rII* region was instrumental in the development of several of our ideas concerning the molecular basis of heredity. We discussed some of these in Chapter 5; we'll look at others in Chapter 10. Let's look now at its contribution to our understanding of the relationship between linkage maps and chromosomes.

One of the more promising aspects of the genetic analysis of a small region, like the *rII* region, is that it can lead to a detailed identification of landmarks (loci) and distances on a map in terms of the structure of DNA. Benzer emphasized the point that geneticists rely upon three distinctly different kinds of operations in their investigations of genic material. (1) Their studies of mutation lead them to hypothesize a smallest segment of genic material that can undergo mutation independently of other segments (a muton). (2) Recombination analysis suggests segments of genic material between which recombination can occur but within any one of which it cannot (a recon). (3) Experiments (described in Chapter 10) that seek to define segments of independent function lead to the concept of the cistron. (The word *gene* has been used throughout the last half century to refer variously to one or another of these units.)

In Chapter 5, we presented chemical reasons for supposing that each nucleotide pair can mutate without concomitant mutation of any other pairs. We'll let this very reasonable notion stand.

No features of the Watson–Crick model for DNA suggest that a recon is other than a single base pair. The following observations lead to an experimental estimate within a factor of two of this.

The minimal recombinant frequency for phage T4 seems to be

about 1×10^{-4}. This value corresponds to approximately 5×10^{-6} of the total map length (see Problem 8.3). Since an upper limit to the size of the T4 chromosome is 2×10^5 nucleotide pairs, it seems likely that recombination can occur between any two adjacent nucleotides. The recon appears to be the same size as the muton.

About 7 per cent of spontaneously occurring *rII* mutations clearly involve alterations more extensive than a single base pair. The most conveniently determined property of high diagnostic value for these mutations is their apparent inability to undergo reverse mutation; their reverse mutation rate is certainly less than 10^{-10}. When these multisite mutants are employed in crosses, they give frequencies of recombinants indicative of their gross nature; they fail to produce wild-type recombinants with each of the members of a map sequence of markers all of which *do* recombine with each other. The presumptive molecular basis of these multisite mutants has been determined in several instances. The frequency of particles recombinant for loci r_a and r_b was measured in crosses of the following sort:

$$\text{I} \qquad \frac{r_a \; r_m^+ \; r_b^+}{\times \atop r_a^+ \; r_m^+ \; r_b} \qquad \text{and} \qquad \text{II} \qquad \frac{r_a \; r_m \; r_b^+}{\times \atop r_a^+ \; r_m \; r_b}$$

where r_m is the multisite mutant and r_m^+ is its wild-type allele; loci r_a and r_b are each close to r_m. Crosses of type II give lower frequencies of recombinants for loci r_a and r_b indicating that the multisite mutations are deletions. Measurements of the density of these multisite mutant particles, however, fail to reveal a decreased DNA content. Streisinger and his associates have shown that the terminal redundancy in r_m-mutant particles is compensatorily longer than in r_m^+ particles.

Crosses involving only deletions in the *rII* region have provided an operationally unique demonstration of the one-dimensionality of a linkage map over relatively short distances. Two deletions that invade a common region of the map fail to give recombinants (by definition) when crossed with each other. In a one-dimensional map the relative positions of each of a number of deletions can be represented, for instance, like this:

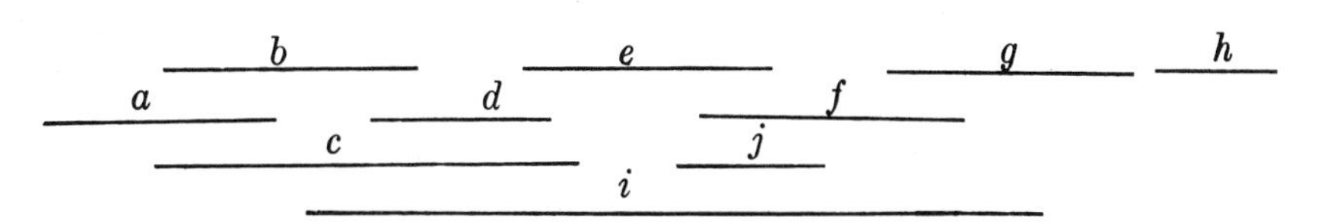

Such an array derives from the results of all the possible two-factor crosses shown at the top of the following page.

other parent (columns); one parent (rows)

	a	b	c	d	e	f	g	h	i	j
a	0	0	0	+	+	+	+	+	+	+
b		0	0	0	+	+	+	+	0	+
c			0	0	0	+	+	+	0	+
d				0	0	+	+	+	0	+
e					0	0	+	+	0	0
f						0	0	+	0	0
g							0	+	0	+
h								0	+	+
i									0	0
j										0

+ = some wild-type recombinants produced.

0 = no wild-type recombinants produced.

Is any other array compatible with these data?

Enthusiastic extension of this approach is notable for its failure to uncover a single matrix like that shown below left. Convince yourself that this significant failure tends to rule out topological map relationships of the sort shown below right.

	w	x	y	z
w	0	0	+	0
x		0	0	+
y			0	0
z				0

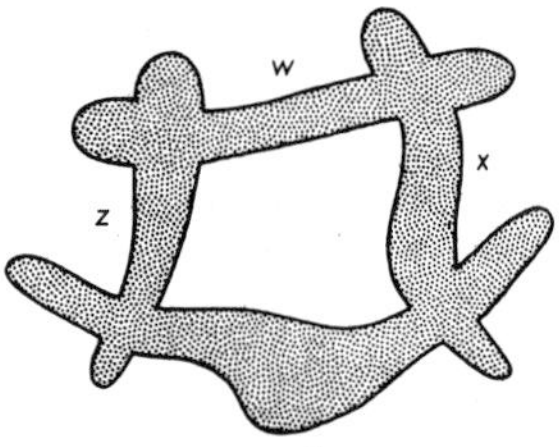

There is no need to involve two dimensions when constructing a map by this (or any other) procedure.

Recombination in RNA viruses

Genetic recombination has been studied in viruses other than phage. Of special interest is the demonstration in the early 1960's that the RNA virus that causes polio undergoes recombination.

Summary

The study of recombination among viruses holds promise of elucidating the molecular mechanism of recombination. The populational aspects of many virus experiments appear to offset some of the advantages. However, the "irregularities" in segregation and recombination among higher organisms may have an explanation in terms of local outbursts of populational recombination. The next chapter bears distinct implications of this sort.

References

Levinthal, Cyrus, "Bacteriophage Genetics" in *The Viruses II* (New York: Academic Press, Inc., 1959), pp. 281-317. A clear, though somewhat outdated, review of the principal facts of phage recombination.

Meselson, M. S., and J. J. Weigle, "Chromosome Breakage Accompanying Genetic Recombination in Bacteriophage," *Proc. Nat. Acad. Sci. U.S.*, *47* (1961), 857-68. An elegant little classic, simple and profound.

Steinberg, Charley, and Frank Stahl, "The Theory of Formal Phage Genetics," *Cold Spring Harbor Symp. Quant. Biol.*, *23* (1958), 42-45. A generalized consideration of the population aspects of a phage cross.

Problems

8.1. Consider a population of chromosomes mating in pairs randomly in time and without regard to genotype. (As in the Visconti–Delbrück theory.) Let the initial constitution of the population be exactly equal numbers of abc and $+++$.

(a) If markers a and c are so far apart as to be essentially unlinked on an ordinary linear map, what is the average number of matings per particle required to give in the population 34% recombinants between a and c?

(b) To give exactly 50% recombinants?

(c) If a and b show 4% recombinants when a and c show 34%, what is the probability per elementary act of recombination between a and b?

(d) How many rounds of mating will have occurred when a and b show 12% recombinants?

(e) What per cent recombination will a and c show at that time?

8.2. In a certain phage three linked loci give R values like this under the condition of equal frequencies of the two infecting types:

$$\frac{a \overset{.075}{\quad} b \overset{0.10}{\quad} c}{.135}$$

Let us define an index of coincidence, i, by the equation

$$R_{ac} = R_{ab} + R_{bc} - 2iR_{ab}R_{bc}\ [8]$$

[8] For phage T4, i is about 1.5 when R_{ab} and R_{bc} are about 0.05 or larger High negative interference is signaled by the larger i values that occur when pairs of loci giving smaller R values are studied. Values of i as large as 30 have been measured in three-factor crosses employing the analogous expression:

observed frequency of double recombinants $= iR_{ab}R_{bc}$.

(a) Calculate the index of coincidence for the map of these loci.

(b) Suppose the phage in question undergoes an average of one round of mating per lineage. Ignore the spread in maturation times and the fluctuation from cell to cell in input frequencies and calculate p, the probability of recombination per mating act for each of the three intervals.

(c) Calculate the coefficient of coincidence relating these p values.

(d) Calculate the map distance, d, between each pair of loci. Test the d values for additivity. Compare your answers with the appropriate curve in Fig. 8.1a.

(e) In a set of single mating acts between particles of complementary genotype, what frequency of double recombinants would be produced for the case of the loci discussed above?

8.3. In order to estimate the fraction of the total map that is occupied by a particular region, a relationship between the frequency of recombinants and map distance must be established. Because of the circularity and high negative interference, the proper mapping function for T4 is quite uncertain. However, there is a relationship that shows promise of working.

Let's ignore the complication of the hypothesized terminal redundancies of the circularly permuted chromosome. Then, each chromosome has a sequence as

a . . . . . z
b . . . . za
c . . . zab
and so forth.

As a null hypothesis we'll suppose that all possible sequences are represented in equal frequencies in a T4 population. For computational convenience, let's switch units and let each chromosome have a length of 1. For a given pair of loci, then, a T4 population can be classified into two groups. In one group the distance between the two loci is D and in the other group the distance is $1-D$. The two groups represent fractions of the total population of $1-D$ and D respectively. We may picture it this way:

Appearance of chromosome	Frequency of chromosome
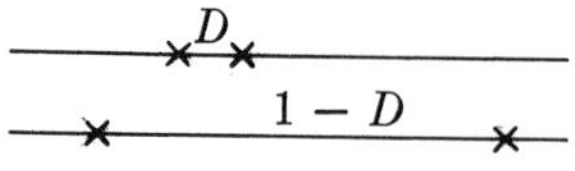 ——×D×————	$1-D$
—×—— $1-D$ ——×—	D

Then the total frequency of recombinants in a mating pool can be written by analogy to the equation (8-5) developed for phage λ:

$$R = \tfrac{1}{2}\{[1-D][1-\exp(-mp_D)] + D[1-\exp(-mp_{(1-D)})]\} \qquad \text{(Eq. 8.6)}$$

where p_D is the probability of recombination per mating act (between phages of complementary genotype) for markers separated by a distance D, and p_{1-D} is the analogous symbol for markers separated by a distance $1-D$.

We must now select a relationship between p and D that accounts for high negative interference. A variety of relationships have been written and tested against the data. The test of whether these functions "work" is their ability to convert observed recombination values ($\overline{R}$) to additive D values. Of those expressions that appear to work, we shall select the one that follows most easily from ideas already presented in this volume.

Let's assume pairing regions (similar to those depicted on page 94 in Chapter 7) of fixed length K. K, like D, is measured as a fraction of a map of unit circumference. Let there be one and only one pairing region in any mating; i.e., with respect to pairing regions there is complete positive interference in each elementary mating act. The only additional assumption we make is that the number of points of exchange is Poisson distributed among pairing regions (with a mean number, x, per region). On the basis of these assumptions we can write (though I leave it for those who like exercise to prove)

$$p_D = \frac{1}{2}(K - D)(1 - e^{-2Dx/K}) + D\left[1 - \frac{1 - e^{-2Dx/K}}{2Dx/K}\right] \quad \text{when} \quad D < K$$

$$p_D = \frac{1}{2}(D - K)(1 - e^{-2x}) + K\left[1 - \frac{1 - e^{-2x}}{2x}\right] \quad \text{when} \quad D > K$$

The mapping function (when averaged for maturation spread) contains the four parameters m_1, m_2, K, and x, where m_1 and m_2 are respectively the average rounds of mating per lineage for the first and last particles to mature. In order to use the function, we must obtain estimates for each of these parameters. This is a formidable task. An approach that worked was to let an electronic computer search for a combination of values that gave good additivity of the D values derived by application of the function. The computer selected the values

$$m_1 = 9$$
$$m_2 = 20$$
$$K = 1.4 \times 10^{-2}$$
$$x = 3$$

when $\overline{R}$ was corrected for finite input (14 infecting phage particles per cell).

(a) For these values of the parameters show that as $D \to 0$, $\overline{R}$ can be written approximately as

$$\overline{R}_{D\to 0} \cong 0.45D(\overline{m}x + 1), \text{ where } \overline{m} = \frac{m_1 + m_2}{2}$$
$$= 20.0D$$

Recall that D is measured as a fraction of a circumference of unit length. Recall also that the genome of T4 contains 2×10^5 nucleotide pairs (or somewhat less).

(b) Calculate the smallest $\overline{R}$ value one would observe in T4 if a recon were equivalent to a single nucleotide pair. The smallest values actually observed are about 1×10^{-4}. It seems likely that a recon is a single nucleotide pair.

8.4. Can you devise an experiment to test whether any phage "heterozygotes" have a chromosomal structure in the "heterozygous" region like either of those on page 65 in Chapter 6?

Nine

Recombination in Bacteria

We have encountered genetic recombination among the bacteria in two previous instances. Bacterial transformation was briefly described for its importance in identifying the molecular basis of heredity. Bacterial conjugation provided a demonstration of the linear organization of chromosomes as revealed through experiments involving the interruption of chromosome transfer. In this chapter we shall examine these two processes further; we shall look also at several other mechanisms for juxtaposing DNA that result in recombination.

Phages and the bacterial chromosome

Not all strains of bacteriophages are fully destructive to their host cells. (This is a simple example of the old observation that *gentle* parasites may enjoy a selective advantage.) The temperate (as opposed to the virulent) strains of phages have two distinct modes of parasitic reproduction. Early in the course of infection of a bacterium a temperate phage chooses between two mutually exclusive paths of development. In some of the infected cells phage development proceeds lytically; a period of DNA duplication is followed by the appearance in the cell of mature phages with lysis occurring soon after. In others of the infected cells one (or sometimes more) of the phage chromosomes becomes added to the bacterial chromosome. Hand in hand with this act of lysogenization[1] the host cell and its descendants-to-be acquire immunity to the lytic phase of phage reproduction; they survive not only that particular infection but also any subsequent infections by the same strain of phage. Different strains differ in the fraction of infections that lead to reduction to this prophage state (the state of the phage following lysogenization). The factors that influence the frequency of reductive responses are described in Hartman and Suskind's *Gene Action* and Jinks's *Extrachromosomal Inheritance,* other volumes in this series. Here we are concerned with the physical nature of the interaction of the phage and bacterial chromosome; it bears on our understanding of DNA duplication, mutation, and recombination, and on the organization of DNA within chromosomes.

A prophage is duplicated along with the bacterial chromosome of its host, and the two daughter prophages are transmitted one into each daughter cell. The attachment of prophage to the bacterial chromosome is typically a secure one; only rarely in the normal course of events does the prophage abandon its liaison and enter the lytic (destructive) phase of its life cycle (see Problem 9.1). For the phage λ, and for several other well-studied strains of temperate phages, the locus of phage attachment is a unique one. In bacterial conjugation experiments the time of transfer of the prophage from an *Hfr* to an F^- cell is the same for each *Hfr* cell in a synchronously mating population of lysogenic (prophage-carrying) cells.

Transduction

When λ does leave the bacterial chromosome and become lytic, the particles that emerge from the host are generally indistinguishable from the particle that lysogenized the ancestor of the unfortunate cell. Rarely, however, particles emerge that differ from λ in two respects. (1) When infecting host cells by themselves, they are rarely able to enter the lysogenic phase and apparently never enter the lytic phase of reproduction (they are defective). (2) When they do become prophage, they may confer upon the cell a hereditary characteristic of the host from which the defective particles emerged. The only part of the bacterial chromosome that λ can so transduce is the region directing the synthesis of enzymes required for the fermentation of the monosaccharide galactose. Reasonable hypotheses for the structures of the chromosomes of transducing particles and transduced cells have been arrived at from recombinational analysis.

The chromosomes of defective, galactose-transducing λ particles (λ*dg*) can multiply normally in the presence of ordinary λ. A cell

[1] *Lysogenization,* as strictly defined, means only that the information for producing phage particles "spontaneously" has become (as a result of infection) one of the hereditary properties of a bacterium. In most instances this is demonstrably a consequence of the addition of a phage chromosome to the chromosome of a host cell. This shouldn't come as a surprise to my readers, but it was exciting news when established by François Jacob and E. L. Wollman in the 1950's.

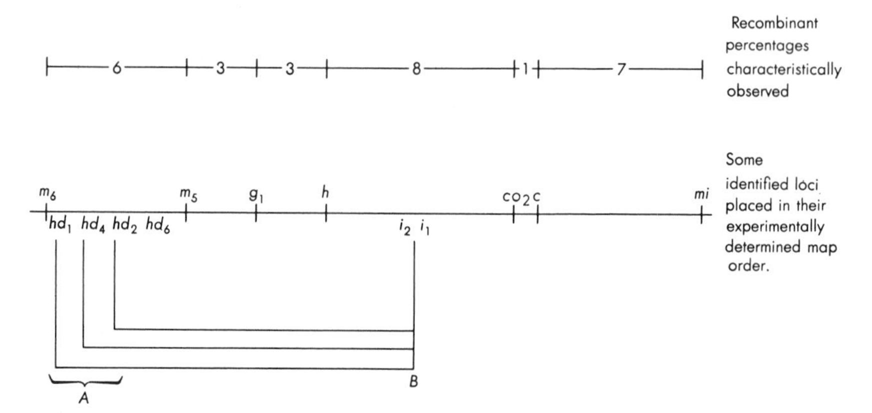

Fig. 9.1. A linkage map of λ indicating the region missing in λ*dg* particles. The defective λ particles that can transduce the *Gal* region of the *coli* chromosome appear by genetic tests to be missing the region of the λ chromosome that corresponds to the part of the linkage map between *A* and *B* in the figure. The *A* end of the region has been demonstrated to vary from one λ*dg* strain to another. The *B* end, on the other hand, has shown no sign of variability.

jointly infected with both kinds of particles may enter either the lysogenic or the lytic cycle of phage production. If the lysogenic mode is adopted, the cell may become lysogenic for both λ*dg* and λ. If it enters the lytic phase, it produces essentially equal numbers of the two kinds of particles. We shall examine the consequences of the lytic response first.

The map of λ*dg* can be determined from the results of crosses between lytic phase λ*dg* and λ particles marked at a number of loci. The map sequence of loci for λ*dg* is identical to that for λ except that a stretch of the map to the "left" of center is "missing"; the λ particles emerging from the cross carry each of the markers of the λ*dg* except for markers at those loci in the missing region. The defectiveness and the transducing capability of λ*dg* particles seem to have a simple common cause. It appears that λ*dg* has exchanged a stretch of its own chromosome for the galactose region of the chromosome of its host.

The portion of the λ map missing from λ*dg* particles varies. Whereas λ*dg* particles in a given clone are exactly alike, particles of independent origin may differ with respect to the length of the missing region of the map. It appears that one end of the missing region may be fixed while the other end is somewhat variable (see Fig. 9.1). This variability contributes to an observed difference in DNA/protein content (as inferred from density measurements) among mature particles of various λ*dg* strains. The correlation between map length of a missing segment and density is rather weak, however, suggesting that the length of the inserted piece of bacterial chromosome may be variable as well.

Our understanding of the organization of chromosomes would obviously benefit from a real understanding of the nature of the association of prophage with bacterial chromosome and transducible markers with the phage chromosome. The latter relationship is relatively easy to examine; chromosomes isolated from λ*dg* appear by the applied physical criteria to be as simple as those isolated from λ. Thus, it seems likely that the transducible galactose region represents a physically ordinary stretch of the single DNA molecule that is the chromosome.

The physical relationship of prophage to the bacterial chromosome is less certain than is the relationship of transducing DNA to the chromosome of phage particles. At this time there appears to be no compelling reason to reject the structurally simple view that the prophage is inserted into the bacterial chromosome; i.e., from a physical point of view, the chromosome of a lysogenic cell differs from that of a corresponding nonlysogenic cell only by being a trifle longer.[2]

The details of the mechanism of reduction or of λ*dg* formation are at present as obscure as are those for the mechanism of crossing over. It seems likely, however, that the two phenomena are related; reduction may occur via crossing over. Figure 9.2 suggests one way in which crossing over between bacterial and phage chromosomes could result in reduction. A "circularized" λ chromosome could undergo one reciprocal crossover with the *coli* chromosome. On this hypothesis, doubly lysogenic cells carry two prophages in tandem in their chromosomes. Allan Campbell in the early 1960's proposed this idea and pointed out some of its advantages. (1) The mechanism of reduction is a "simple" one invoking no novel phenomena. (2) The bacterial chromosome is not physically cluttered by its carried prophages. (3) The formation of λ*dg* particles is not difficult to picture within this scheme (see Fig. 9.3). (4) Results on recombination in λ prophages are rather easily explained.

Two possibilities for recombination between prophages provide bases for study. (1) Prophage recombination can occur as a result of conjugation between two lysogenic strains of *coli* (one an F^- and the other an *Hfr*). Among the descendants of the exconjugant F^- cells some cells can be found that are carrying a recombinant prophage. (2) Cells lysogenic for two complementarily marked strains of λ occasionally give rise to singly lysogenic cells. The prophage carried by this cell may be genetically recombinant.

From these two possibilities for recombination of λ prophage two kinds of rudimentary maps have been made. Both kinds of maps indicate that the order of loci in λ prophage is different from that for lytically duplicating (vegetative) λ. Both are compatible with the

[2] By several criteria λ does not seem to replace any of the host chromosome when lysogenizing. (1) The occasional cell strains that have lost their λ prophage are indistinguishable by all pertinent criteria from corresponding strains that have never been lysogenized. In particular, such "cured" strains are capable of being relysogenized, and the new lysogenic strain is indistinguishable from the original one. (2) No hereditary "defectiveness" is associated with lysogenization by λ. We shall see later that clearly contrary evidence exists for a recently investigated phage quite unrelated to λ.

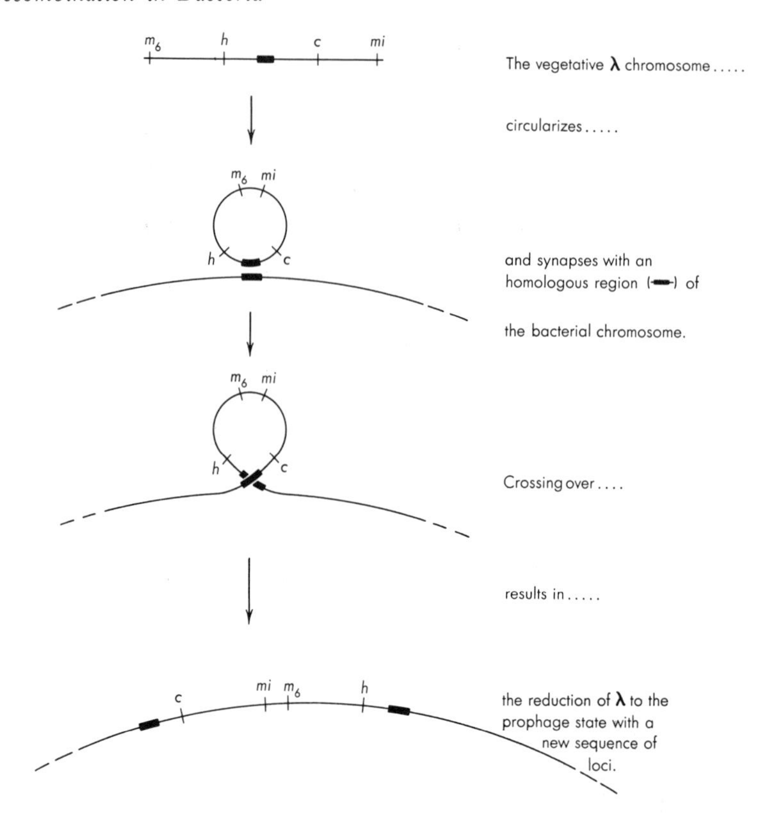

Fig. 9.2. A suggested mechanism for the reduction of λ to the prophage state as proposed by Allan Campbell in the early 1960's. Induction of λ is supposed to result from reversal of the reaction shown above. Double lysogens result from reiteration of the process with the result that the two prophages lie in tandem in the bacterial chromosome.

notion that the order of loci on λ prophage is related to that on vegetative λ by a simple rule: the two maps are circular permutations of each other. The idea of a circular intermediate, which was attractive for its adaptability to the crossover hypotheses of reduction, is useful in providing an explanation for the difference in locus sequence between vegetative and prophage λ. The region between the bacterial chromosome and the (hypothetical) circular λ chromosome need only be supposed to be at a different place on the circular λ chromosome from the termini of the linear vegetative chromosome. Figure 9.2 summarizes this set of notions.

Within the framework of these notions, Campbell has suggested a mechanism for the formation of λ*dg*. The loop that forms prior to the crossover resulting in the elimination of the λ chromosome from the bacterial chromosome (Fig. 9.2) slips so that crossing over occurs where it shouldn't (Fig. 9.3).

The reversibility of the incorporation of λ into the bacterial chromosome illustrates the possibility that many different bits of chromosome

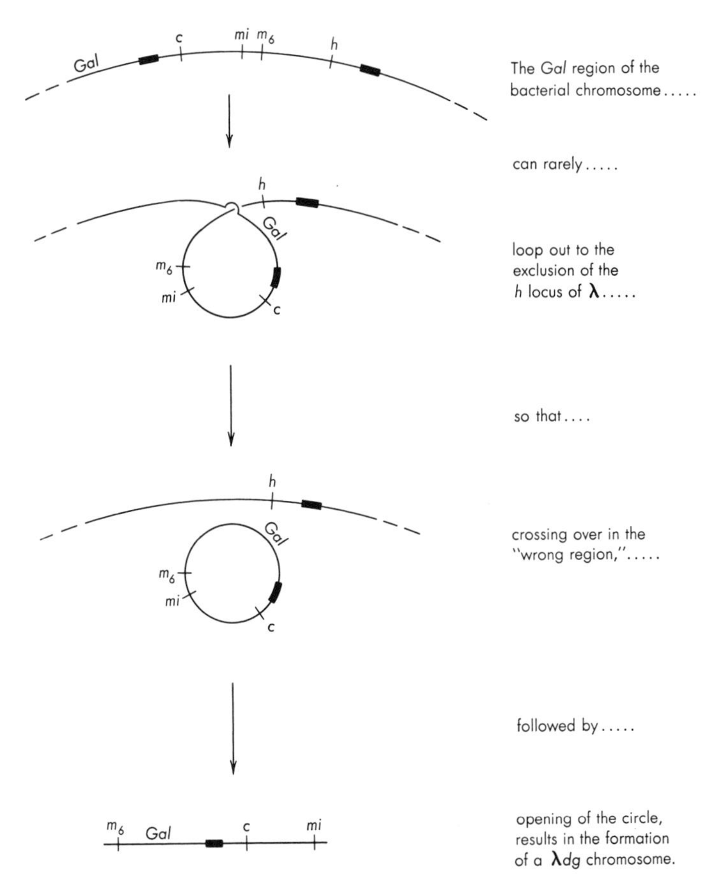

Fig. 9.3. A suggested mechanism for the formation of λ particles able to transduce the *Gal* region of its bacterial host (after a proposal by Allan Campbell in the early 1960's). According to this scheme, λ*dg* formation is the result of a slipshod reversal of the reduction reaction (cf. Fig. 9.2). The imprecision of the event is reflected in the variability from strain to strain of the end of the incorporated *Gal* region that lies close to m_6 (see Fig. 9.1).

can cut in and out. While off the chromosome they may multiply extravagantly and even undergo recombination with their homologues, which may be either at home or on the town at that time. Explanations of negative interference and non-2 : 2 segregations in higher organisms may eventually be found within the framework of such ideas. In the meantime, the concept has proved valuable in a number of phases of bacterial genetics. The significance of part-time chromosomal residents was emphasized by François Jacob and E. L. Wollman in the late 1950's; they called such segments of genic material episomes. Since episomes are (by definition) part-time inhabitants of the cytoplasm, they will come under discussion again in *Extrachromosomal Inheritance* in this series.

There is a style of transduction recognizably different from transduction by λ*dg*. Generalized transducers are temperate phages that can transduce any more or less short stretch of a host-cell chromosome. As in the case of λ, the transducing particles have been demonstrated to be defective for some phages.

One phage that can induce hereditary alterations at (apparently) any locus of a bacterial chromosome has been described recently. These changes are not a consequence of transduction; the change induced is independent of the host upon which the phage was last grown. In every case the alteration induced is to a *loss* of a hereditary biochemical capacity. This mutation goes hand in hand with the reduction of the phage to prophage at the mutated locus. Two explanations seem reasonable. (1) The prophage prevents the proper operation of the region of the bacterial chromosome in its immediate vicinity. (2) The phage replaces a stretch of the bacterial chromosome upon becoming incorporated into it. A crossover mechanism like that diagrammed in Fig. 9.4 would have the observed consequences. How might one experimentally distinguish between these two hypotheses?

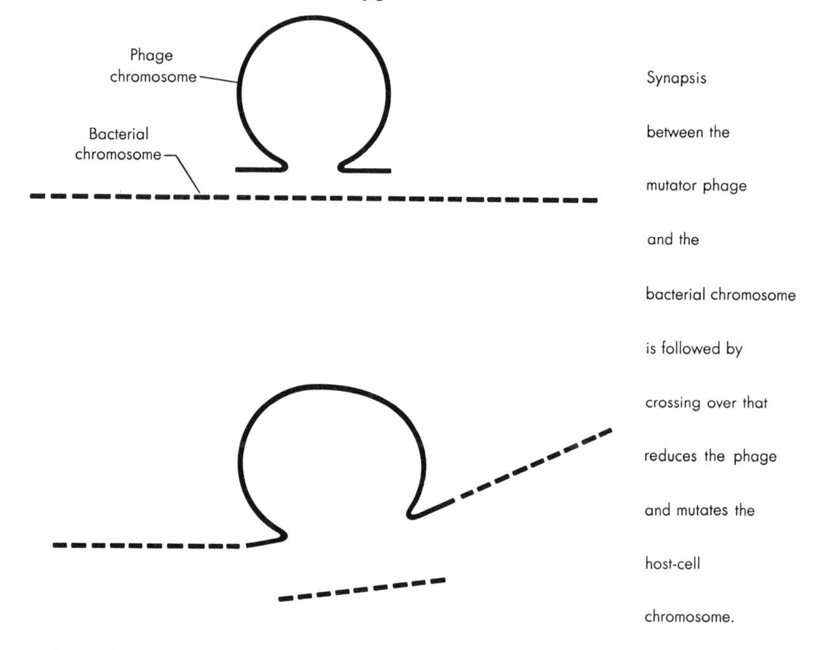

Fig. 9.4. A hypothesized crossover mechanism for reduction of the "mutator" phage mu − 1. The two terminal regions of the phage chromosome synapse and cross over with homologous regions of the bacterial chromosome. A stretch of the bacterial chromosome is thereby replaced by the phage. Since the phage can become resident at any locus, there must be numerous points of homology along the bacterial chromosome. Perhaps these are nucleotide sequences that demark regions (cistrons; see Chapter 10) responsible for the specification of the amino acid sequence of distinct polypeptides.

Episomes in bacterial fertility

In *Escherichia* and related genera the ability to conjugate and transfer genic material from cell to cell is dependent upon an episome. Cells that harbor this episome (the F factor) extrachromosomally are capable of becoming fertile (*Hfr*) donors of genic material. The change from an F carrying (F^+) cell to an *Hfr* cell is a mutational one. The F factors disappear from their extrachromosomal location and one of them assumes a chromosomal residence. Hand in hand with the reduction of the F factor the cell becomes a fertile donor; furthermore, the descendants of this cell are *Hfr* as well. Each independently isolated *Hfr* strain differs from the others; the sequence of marker transfer during conjugation is a characteristic of the strain. The transfer sequences of all the isolated strains are demonstrably related to each other by a simple rule: each sequence can be derived by "cutting" a common hypothetical circular chromosome at the appropriate place. Of the two ends resulting from the cut, one is determined to be the leading end at the time of reduction. Contrary to naïve expectation, for each *Hfr* strain the F factor is the *last* marker to be transferred during conjugation.

In accord with naïve expectation, on the other hand, is evidence indicating that the *coli* chromosome really *is* circular except during the period when it is migrating through the conjugation tube. This evidence was obtained from autoradiographs of carefully isolated chromosomes and from linkage data. The autoradiographs speak for themselves (see Fig. 9.5); the linkage data need but a few words of description and explanation. When care is taken to avoid interruption of conjugation, the entire chromosome of an *Hfr* cell may be transferred into the cell with which it is paired. Among the descendants of the recipient cell, markers on the first and last chromosomal regions to be transferred are typically inherited together. The degree of linkage between them is greater than the linkage of either of the markers to other markers transferred at intermediate times—the linkage map of *E. coli* as derived from the linkage data of a single cross is circular.

The "mechanism" of recombination in bacteria

The kinetics of recombination occurring as a consequence of both conjugation and transformation have been examined. Reasonably enough, the kinetics for the two cases are compatible with the same view. Let's examine the transformation experiments.

M. S. Fox, with R. D. Hotchkiss, in the early 1960's examined the fate of transforming DNA. The events that led to the hereditary alteration of the chromosome of the recipient cell were followed in three kinds of experiments. Each of the experiments involved extraction of DNA from a recipient culture. The extracted DNA was examined for its transforming activity of both the introduced marker and for markers already resident in the recipient cell. The results of all three sets of observations led to a common conclusion: both chains of the transforming DNA are incorporated together without either concomitant or prior duplication of the transforming fragment or the recipient chromosome. The observations were these:

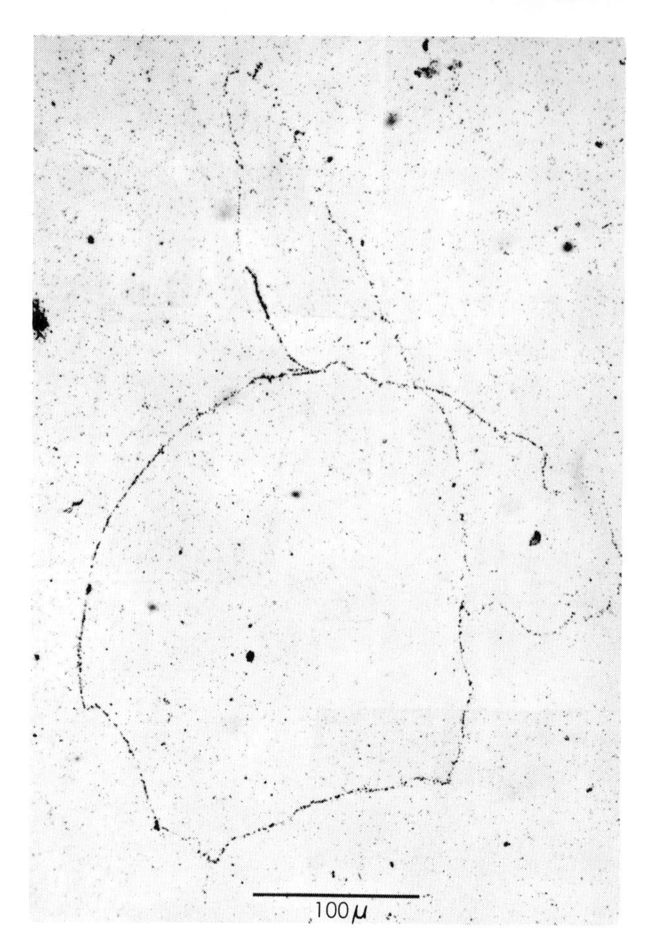

Fig. 9.5. An autoradiograph of a tritium-labeled chromosome of *E. coli*. This chromosome, which was caught in the act of duplicating, was extracted from a cell grown for two to three generations in medium containing tritiated thymidine. The solution to the Chinese puzzle implied by this picture is left to the reader to hypothesize and to future research to provide. This photograph was kindly supplied by John Cairns.

(1) The activity of transforming DNA was not recoverable for the first few minutes after "fixation" by the recipient cells. (Fixation is defined as the acquisition of resistance to the destructive action of deoxyribonuclease added to the culture medium.) As soon as the transforming activity was recoverable, it was observed to be increasing at the same rate as other markers already resident at different loci. This situation was established in a small fraction of a generation time.

(2) The frequency with which two close markers undergo joint transformation can be defined as the degree of linkage between them. Shortly after transforming markers were recoverable from a recipient population, they had established normal linkage relationships with nearby markers.

(3) P^{32}-labeled DNA loses transforming activity as a function of the number of P^{32} atoms that have decayed. Labeled DNA was used for transformation and then the suicide sensitivity of the transforming activity of DNA was reisolated after the full establishment of normal linkage relationships with resident markers was determined. The sensitivity was essentially the same as that in the initial transforming DNA preparation.

Convince yourself that these observations support the conclusion. The conclusion is congruent with that derived from the studies of heavy isotope transfer in λ crosses (Chapter 8).

Summary

A variety of biological mechanisms leading to intimate interactions between stretches of DNA have been observed among bacteria. There is not space here to explore in full this delightful natural history. Jacob and Wollman have done it well in their recent study (see References below). Our principal conclusions are as follows: (1) The molecular mechanisms of recombination have not been revealed from studies of recombination in bacteria, but (2) results from bacterial genetics are fully consonant with those from the genetics of viruses on the one hand and higher organisms on the other.

References

Campbell, Allan, "Episomes," *Adv. Genet., 11* (1962), 101-45. Our knowledge of DNA interactions leading to recombination in bacteria is reviewed within the framework of the episome concept.

Fox, M. S., "The Fate of Transforming Deoxyribonucleate Following Fixation by Transformable Bacteria, III," *Proc. Nat. Acad. Sci. U.S., 48* (1962), 1043-48. The analysis of transforming activity of DNA recovered from recipient cells strongly suggests that recombination occurs by a "break-reunion" mechanism involving simultaneously both chains of both the recipient and the transforming DNA.

——— and R. D. Hotchkiss, "The Fate of Transforming Deoxyribonucleate Following Fixation by Transformable Bacteria, I and II," *Nature, 187* (1960), 1002-06.

Jacob, François, and E. L. Wollman, *Sexuality and the Genetics of Bacteria.* New York: Academic Press, Inc., 1961. This book discusses in detail bacterial recombination and lysogenization as illustrated by the outstanding work of two microbial geneticists.

Tomizawa, Jun-Ichi, "Genetic Structure of Recombinant Chromosomes Formed After Mating in *Escherichia coli* K12," *Proc. Nat. Acad. Sci. U.S., 46* (1960), 91-101. If I have succeeded, the reader will enjoy and perhaps even understand this intellectual tour de force.

Weigle, J. J., M. S. Meselson, and Kenneth Paigen, "Density Alterations Associated with Transducing Ability in the Bacteriophage Lambda," *J. Mol. Biol., 1* (1959), 379-86. Transducing λ particles are not only defective but have a DNA content different from that of normal λ.

Problems

9.1. A bacterial strain can be called lysogenic only if occasional cells release infectious phage particles. (This statement implies a corollary; many, perhaps most (or all!) bacterial strains carry prophage-like chromosomal symbionts that remain undetected because of their failure

to escape from the host-cell chromosome and be released as infectious virus.) The rate of release of phages by lysogenic cells can be measured. This problem illustrates one method of determining this rate.
(a) Suppose that a lysogenic culture is adjusted to a concentration of 100 cells per ml. One ml. volumes are then delivered into each of a large number of tubes. Each of these cultures is then permitted to grow to a concentration of 10^6 cells per ml. At that point each tube is examined for the presence of mature, infectious phage particles. 87 per cent of the tubes are found to contain some extracellular phage particles. Calculate the probability of phage release per cell per duplication.
(b) The rate of phage release by the cells of a lysogenic culture can be altered by environmental agents. Ultraviolet light (UV) is a convenient agent for inducing lysogenic cells to liberate phages. A cell induced by UV lyses as a consequence of phage production. UV is lethal to bacterial cells for other reasons; the proper functioning of DNA is generally sensitive to UV. For the (hypothetical) results described below calculate the fraction of cell-lethal hits that are a result of phage induction. Your answer, I trust, confirms the typical conclusion that UV killing of lysogenic cells by induction is far greater than all the other sources of UV killing combined.

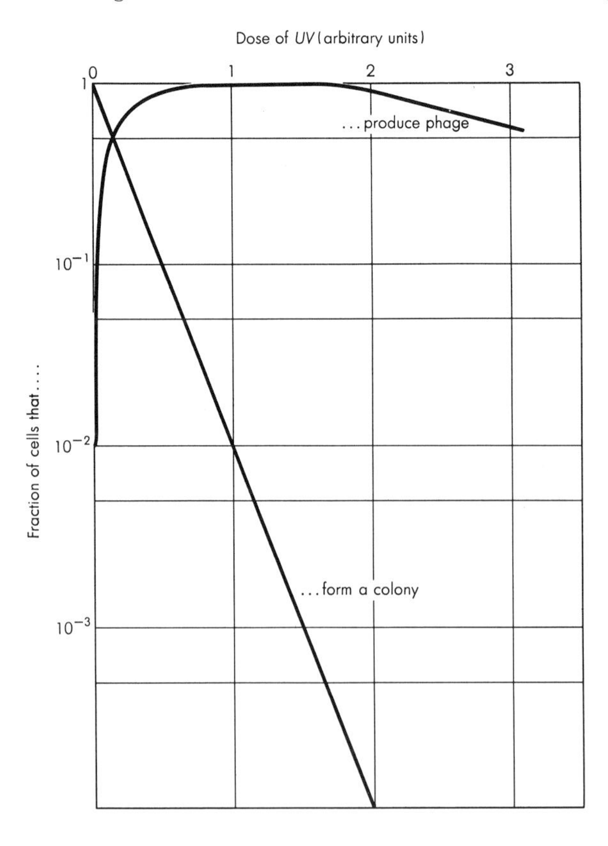

9.2. It is sometimes difficult to sustain conjugation in *E. coli* long enough for the entire genome to be transmitted from donor to recipient. Thus, in some crosses of an *Hfr* strain by an F− strain, the linkage relations of only a fraction of the genetic markers distinguishing the two strains may be determined. Suppose that in such crosses the following *Hfr* strains donate the markers shown in the order written. (The order can be determined by interrupting conjugation with an electric blender, by determining P^{32} sensitivity of the markers prior to conjugation, or by scoring the frequencies of the various recombinant classes among the offspring of the recipient cells.)

Hfr strain	*Markers donated in order*				
1	*Q*	*W*	*D*	*M*	*T*
2	*A*	*X*	*P*	*T*	*M*
3	*B*	*N*	*C*	*A*	*X*
4	*B*	*Q*	*W*	*D*	*M*

Draw the presumptive sequence of markers in the F+ strain from which these *Hfr* strains were derived.

9.3. From an F+ *coli* strain of genotype A^+ B^- *CDEG*, 2 *Hfr* strains were isolated. Each of these was made radioactive to the same degree with P^{32}, and decay of P^{32} was permitted to proceed while the *Hfr* cells were frozen. At intervals, samples of each strain were thawed and mated with F− cells of genotype A^- B^+ *cdeg*. The zygotes were plated on a medium upon which only A^+ B^+ cells could form colonies. The colonies formed were scored for the presence of the genetic markers *C*, *D*, *E*, and *G* from the *Hfr* parent. The results of these experiments for the two strains are given in the figure below.

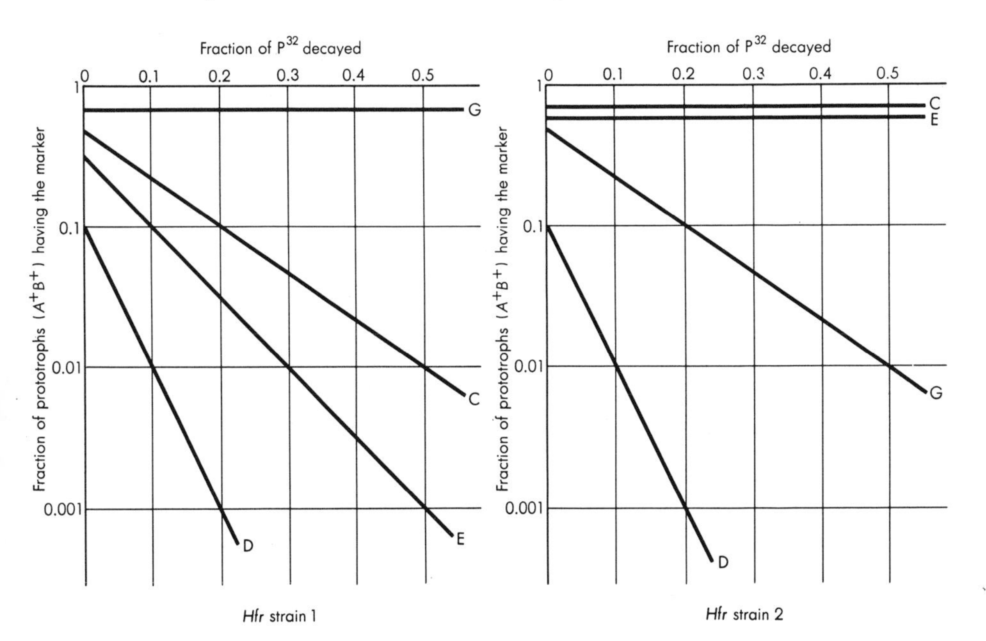

From these data draw a "linkage map" for the F+ strain. This map should show the sequence of the loci (*A*, *C*, *D*, *E*, *G*, but not necessarily of *B*) and the point of origin and direction of transfer of each *Hfr* strain.

(a) What fraction of the total chromosome lies between loci *A* and *D* in *Hfr* strains numbers 1 and 2?

(b) Determine the fraction of the chromosome that lies between each of the following pairs of loci along the shorter arc of the circular map: *D–G*, *C–D*, *C–G*, and *C–E*.

9.4. A student has a strain (2) of bacteria that is resistant to drugs *A*, *B*, *C*, and *D*. He also has the sensitive strain (1) from which the resistant strain was derived by 4 independent mutational steps. He can extract DNA from strain 2 and apply it to strain 1. Then, he can plate the treated cells of strain 1 on agar containing various combinations of the drugs. Suppose he does that with the following results:

Drug added to agar	*Number of colonies*	*Drug added to agar*	*Number of colonies*
None	10,000	*BC*	51
A	1,156	*BD*	49
B	1,148	*CD*	786
C	1,161	*ABC*	30
D	1,139	*ABD*	42
AB	46	*ACD*	630
AC	640	*BCD*	36
AD	942	*ABCD*	30

He concludes that three of the factors for drug resistance are linked to each other and the fourth is not linked to those three.

(a) Which factor is *not* linked?

(b) In what *order* do the three linked factors occur on their DNA molecule?

The Genetic Analysis of Diploids

This last chapter will serve several purposes. It will provide a partial review of ideas introduced in previous chapters. It will provide a bridge to Hartman and Suskind's *Gene Action* as well as to other volumes in this series. It will provide a point of departure for students who wish to read in the early literature of genetics.

Genotype and phenotype

The genetic markers carried by an individual constitute its genotype. In the examples used to this point, the genotype of each individual was generally deducible from a glance at the appearance (the phenotype) of the individual. In this chapter we shall deal frequently with exceptions to this situation.

Phenotypic lag and phenotypic mixing

The distinction between genotype and phenotype is conveniently emphasized by one phenomenon occurring in bacteria and another occurring among phages.

When a mutation occurs in a multiplying bacterial population, several generations may pass before individuals of mutant phenotype appear. Two sources of this phenotypic lag can be easily identified for the case of a mutation from prototrophy to auxotrophy. (1) A bacterial cell that mutates to the inability to produce a certain enzyme may give rise for several generations to progeny cells that contain enzyme molecules partitioned out to them at the time of cell division. Such cells will manifest nutritional properties like those of their prototrophic ancestor, even though essentially all of their descendants are destined to be auxotrophic. These cells are genotypically auxotrophic but have a prototrophic phenotype. (2) Under some conditions of growth, many strains of bacteria are "multi-nucleate"; each cell possesses more than one set of genic material (see Fig. 6.8). Clearly, the phenotypic manifestation of a mutation to auxotrophy in one of these chromosomes must await the partitioning of that chromosome into a cell that contains no nonmutant chromosomes.[1] Please note that our analysis of mutation in bacterial populations in Chapter 1 ignored phenotypic lag.

Mutants of phages are known that produce altered structural components of their protein "coats." When mutant and wild-type phages are grown in the same bacterial cell, the emerging particles possess protein coats the components of which are drawn without regard to the genotype of the particle from a pool of mutant and wild-type protein molecules. Particles with such mixed coats may manifest some properties characteristic of one or the other (or both) phage strains while other properties may be intermediate between those of the two strains. Phenotypic mixing has been detected for stability at high temperatures, serological properties, and for the ability of particles to attach to different strains of bacteria, as well as for other properties that depend on the protein moiety of mature phage particles.

Dominance and recessiveness

The phenotype of a phage-infected cell is a reflection of the genotype of the particle that initiates the infection. For instance, *rII* mutants of T4 fail to complete an infectious cycle when they infect prophage-carrying strains of *E. coli*. Wild-type (rII^+) phages, on the other hand, can develop normally in such *coli* strains. What is the phenotype of a cell infected with one particle of each genotype? Such infected cells have a wild-type phenotype; they produce a full crop of phage particles (half of which have the *rII* genotype and half of which are rII^+). Under these conditions the presence of the rII^+ determines the phenotype; the rII^+ marker is said to be dominant relative to its recessive *rII* allele. The dominance of rII^+ is not absolute. If a single rII^+ particle infects *coli* (λ) along with *several rII* particles, the infected cell often *fails* to produce phages.

Nature and nurture

The phenotype of an individual is a function not only of its genotype but also of the environment in which the creature develops. Phages of the *rII* genotype have a *lethal* phenotype when developing

[1] The rationale for occasional exceptions to this simple behavior is developed in *Gene Action*.

in *coli* (λ), but they develop perfectly well in *coli* cells that do not harbor λ. The lethal phenotype of *rII* mutants in *coli* (λ) is itself subject to further environmental modification. If the infection proceeds in a medium of high magnesium ion concentration the *rII* phages develop normally.

Complementation

Mutants of T4 are known that can complete every step in their life cycle except for the "last" one. These mutants (*e* mutants) fail to produce a sufficiently active form of the enzyme (lysozyme) that digests the wall of the host cell permitting the escape of the particles. (Such mutants can be propagated by the geneticist who adds lysozyme to the growth medium.) Cells jointly infected by *e* and e^+ particles lyse normally as a result of the action of the wild-type enzyme produced by the chromosome of e^+ genotype. (With respect to the phenotype "cellular lysis," e^+ is dominant over *e*. Partial dominance may be apparent at the molecular level; the infected cell may contain both wild-type lysozyme and the defective lysozyme characteristically produced in cells infected by the *e* mutant only.) *E. coli* (λ) infected by *either* $rIIe^+$ or rII^+e particles fail to release phages. Cells infected simultaneously by particles of these two genotypes, however, produce and release a full crop of phages; the two genotypes complement each other.

Many distinguishable *rII* mutants have been identified (see Chapters 5 and 8). These mutations all occur within one region of the linkage map of T4 (Fig. 8.3). The *rII* region comprises about 1 per cent of the total map. Similarly, a number of *e* mutants, distinguishable by rates of back mutation and by recombination, have been studied. These mutants, too, fall in one small region, which has a length less than 1 per cent of the whole map. Infection of a bacterium by two different *e* mutants usually does not lead to the release of phage particles; *e* mutants show little or no complementation with each other. A cistron (named by Seymour Benzer, mid 1950's) is a region of a chromosome within which complementation typically fails to occur. The *e* region is composed of but one cistron. Mixed infections of *E. coli* (λ) by different pairs of *rII* mutants, on the other hand, often do result in the production of a full crop of phages. The mutants fall into groups A and B. Mutant pairs within a group show little or no complementation, but pairs composed of members from different groups show full complementation. The results of crosses show that the A and B mutants fall in *separate,* but adjacent, regions of the map. The *rII* region is, therefore, composed of two cistrons.

That complementation occurs between all rII^+e and $rIIe^+$ mutants suggests that the two regions of the chromosome corresponding to the *rII* and *e* regions of the linkage map perform separate genic functions. Presumably the two regions specify the sequence of amino acids in different proteins. It seems likely that a cistron corresponds to a stretch of DNA that codes for the amino acid sequence of one kind of polypeptide chain. There is much more about cistrons in Hartman and Suskind's *Gene Action*.

It is not the purpose of this volume to expose in full the physiological basis of the relationships between environment, genotype, and phenotype. They were described for the *rII* and *e* mutants of T4 in order to establish (and qualify) some definitions that facilitate further discussion.

Heterozygosis in bacteria

Among bacteria there are several situations known in which allelic markers coexist in a stable fashion in individual cells. As we have seen (Chapter 9), Gal^- cells transduced to Gal^+ phenotype by λdg typically carry both Gal^- and Gal^+ alleles. Such cells have been termed heterogenotes.

Under some circumstances, large parts of a *coli* chromosome transferred during conjugation can coexist in the recipient cell with the original chromosome. The phenotype of such partial diploids illustrates in the expected fashion the phenomena of dominance, recessiveness, and complementation.

These partial diploids are heterozygous for those loci at which the donor and recipient cells carried different alleles. They are quite comparable to the diploid cells (heterozygotes) that arise by union of genetically different gametes in higher organisms.

Diploidy in higher organisms

In essentially all of the higher organisms, the formation of completely diploid cells is a regular feature of the life cycle. In some of these (e.g., *Chlamydomonas*), the diplophase is transient and unexpressive; its phenotype is to an appreciable extent independent of its *particular* genotype. For the majority of the higher organisms, however, the diplophase is more persistent. Among the more familiar creatures (cats, firs, Drosophila) the diplophase is the conspicuous stage in the life cycle. Indeed, in these creatures the haplophase is highly unexpressive.[2] In such organisms, however, the genotypes of diploid individuals and their haploid meiotic products can generally be deduced from hybridization experiments. The rules for the conduct of good hybridization experiments were set by example by Gregor Mendel in the 1860's.

(1) Hereditary characteristics that can be scored with minimal ambiguity should be selected for study.

(2) For each locus of potential interest in the strains to be analyzed, the likelihood that the same marker is carried on each of the homolo-

[2] In some creatures (yeast, for instance) both the diplophase and the haplophase can be propogated as single cells. The transition to diplophase can result from cellular fusion followed by nuclear fusion. Haploidization results from meiosis. This is an experimentally convenient situation, and the student ought to have no trouble reconstructing its genetic analysis.

gous chromosomes should be maximized. This homozygosity can be made likely by employing individuals descended from a large number of generations of matings between phenotypically similar siblings (i.e., by inbreeding). The effect of inbreeding on homozygosity is described in detail in Brewbaker's *Agricultural Genetics* in this series.

(3) The offspring of matings between individuals of two such inbred strains that differ from each other with respect to a few phenotypic characteristics should be selected for examination.

(4) Sibling matings with the hybrids from step three should be performed. Their offspring should be examined for the frequencies of occurrence of each of the possible phenotypes.

(5) It is often useful to mate the hybrids with each of the original inbred strains and examine the offspring of these backcrosses for the frequencies of occurrence of each of the possible phenotypes.

From just such experiments Mendel and the generation of geneticists that rediscovered his methodology in 1900 were able to reveal the phenomena of the union of gametes at random with respect to genotype, segregation, dominance and recessiveness, complementation, recombination (linked and unlinked), interference (positive and negative), and to correlate these phenomena with the behavior of chromosomes. The heroic nature of their triumph is apparent when we realize that the outcome of each one of their experiments was usually determined by the interplay of most of these phenomena, as well as some others. If I have been successful, my readers should find such analysis easy; I doubt that I've been so completely "successful" as to take the fun out of it. Try the problems, please, and we'll see.

Reference

Mendel, Gregor, "Experiments in Plant Hybridization," 1865. Reprinted in *Classic Papers in Genetics*, J. A. Peters, ed. (Englewood Cliffs, N.J.: Prentice-Hall, Inc., 1959), pp. 1-20.

Problems

10.1. Consider an organism which has an alteration of haploid and diploid generations in which the diplophase arises by nuclear fusion between two haploid cells (gametes), and the haploid cells are produced by meiosis. (Such is the case for cats, firs, and *Drosophila*.) Let's suppose that three genetic loci (1, 2, and 3) are known for this creature. Locus 1 can be occupied by marker A or its allele a; locus 2 can be occupied by B or its allele b; locus 3 can be occupied by D or d. Assume that the markers denoted by capital letters are dominant over their alleles, and that the three loci influence phenotype independently of each other. Now consider some diploid individuals all of which were formed by the union of one gamete of type ABD and the other of type abd. (The offspring of matings between two pure-breeding strains are called collectively the F_1.)

(a) Considering just locus 1, what fraction of the haploid cells produced by meiosis in F_1 individuals will be of genotype A?

(b) Considering just locus 1, what genotypes of diploids can arise by random union of gametes produced by F_1 individuals? In what frequencies do the various genotypes arise?

(c) What fraction of the diploids produced in Problem 10.1b have the phenotype *a*?

(d) Considering just loci 1 and 2, what genotypes of gametes can be produced by F_1 individuals? In what frequency do the types occur if loci 1 and 2 are unlinked? if loci 1 and 2 recombine 20 per cent of the time?

(e) Considering just loci 1 and 2, four possible phenotypes of diploids can arise by random union of gametes produced by F_1 individuals (call such offspring the F_2). We designate these as *AB*, *Ab*, *aB*, and *ab* depending on whether they have the phenotype characteristic of the dominant or of the recessive allele at the respective loci. In what frequency do the various phenotypes arise in the F_2 if loci 1 and 2 are unlinked? if loci 1 and 2 recombine 20 per cent of the time?

(f) Suppose that loci 1 and 2 recombine 20 per cent of the time, that loci 2 and 3 recombine 10 per cent of the time, and that loci 1 and 3 recombine more than 20 per cent of the time. For the gametes produced by the F_1 write the genotypes that are recombinant simultaneously for each of the two pairs of neighboring loci. What are the frequencies of each of these double recombinants if the coefficient of coincidence (S) for the two adjacent regions of the map is 0.6? if S is 0?

10.2. Consider an agriculturally important plant heterozygous at four loci. It is known that three of the loci are on one chromosome and that the other one is on a different chromosome. The loci carry allelic pairs of markers determining height (short or tall) at locus 1, leaf color (red or green) at locus 2, leaf texture (rough or smooth) at locus 3, leaf width (narrow or wide) at locus 4. Suppose the heterozygous individuals arose from a cross of a pure-breeding (homozygous) strain that was tall, red, rough, and wide with another homozygous strain that was short, green, smooth, and narrow. In a test cross (a cross of an F_1 to a strain carrying only recessive alleles at all pertinent loci), the following progeny were produced in the indicated (invented) numbers:

Phenotype				*Numbers of individuals*
tall	red	rough	wide	128
short	green	smooth	narrow	134
tall	green	rough	wide	95
short	red	smooth	narrow	93
tall	red	smooth	wide	129
short	green	rough	narrow	133
tall	red	smooth	narrow	21
short	green	rough	wide	17
tall	green	smooth	wide	92
short	red	rough	narrow	96
tall	green	smooth	narrow	5
short	red	rough	wide	7
tall	red	rough	narrow	18
short	green	smooth	wide	20
tall	green	rough	narrow	6
short	red	smooth	wide	6
			Total	1,000

(a) Which locus is on a separate chromosome?
(b) What is the order of the loci on a common chromosome?
(c) What is the frequency of recombination for each of the adjacent loci in Problem 10.2b?
(d) What is the coefficient of coincidence for the neighboring regions of the map?

10.3. Suppose an inbred deep-purple pigeon-toed one was mated with a white normal-toed one. All of their many offspring were violet-colored and normal-toed. When these offspring (the F_1) were mated to individuals of the inbred deep-purple, pigeon-toed strain, offspring were produced in the following frequencies:

Phenotype	*Frequency*
deep-purple, pigeon-toed	0.40
violet-colored, normal-toed	0.40
violet-colored, pigeon-toed	0.10
deep-purple, normal-toed	0.10

It may help you to know that when the F_1 were mated to inbred individuals whose phenotype was white, pigeon-toed, they produced offspring with the frequencies shown below:

Phenotype	*Frequency*
violet-colored, pigeon-toed	0.40
white, normal-toed	0.40
white, pigeon-toed	0.10
violet-colored, normal-toed	0.10

(a) What is the recombination frequency for the two loci involved in this problem?
(b) When F_1 individuals are mated to each other, their offspring are called the F_2. What frequency of violet, normal-toed individuals would you expect to find among the F_2 of this problem? What frequency of white, pigeon-toed individuals?

10.4. Suppose a highly inbred tall, white, long-haired male individual was mated with an inbred short, red, hairless female. All of their offspring were tall, red, and long-haired. Siblings mated to each other produced the following kinds of offspring in the indicated proportions:

Phenotype	*Frequency*
tall, red, long-haired	0.5056
tall, white, long-haired	0.2394
short, red, long-haired	0.0046
tall, red, hairless	0.0042
short, white, long-haired	0.0002
short, red, hairless	0.2354
tall, white, hairless	0.0006
short, white, hairless	0.0096

(a) Calculate the frequency of recombination for each of the two map intervals involved.
(b) Calculate the coefficient of coincidence for the two map intervals.
(c) How might you redesign the experiment so as to extract the same information more easily?

10.5. Perhaps in some plant (such as corn) there exists an enzymatically catalyzed sequence of chemical reactions leading to the formation of a red substance *Z*. The precursors of *Z* are *X* and *Y*, both of which are colorless. The conversion of *X* to *Y* is accomplished by enzyme

E_1, the conversion of Y to Z by enzyme E_2. Two different pure-breeding strains are known which fail to produce red pigment. The F_1 resulting from matings between individuals from the two different strains all produce red pigment. In the F_2 the ratio of red to nonred individuals was observed to be 0.5625 : 0.4375. What is the frequency of recombination between the two loci influencing the production of Z?

Appendix

The Poisson Distribution

Consider a sequence of N trials the outcome of each of which is independent of the outcome of previous trials. Let the probability of success of any one trial be p and that of failure be $1 - p = q$. The probability P_n of exactly n successes in N trials is given by the $(n + 1)$ term of the expansion of the binomial $(p + q)^N$.

$$P_n = \frac{N!}{(N - n)!n!} p^n q^{N-n}$$

Many readers will know this already; others will be content to accept it. For those who fall into neither category, I offer a derivation of sorts.

Consider a bucket containing a vast number of marbles. A fraction p of the marbles are red, and the remaining fraction $q = 1 - p$ are green. Beside the bucket you have an array of N teacups numbered $1 - N$. Stir the contents of the bucket thoroughly, then close your eyes and grab a marble. Transfer the marble to one of the teacups. Now pick a second marble from the bucket and transfer that to a different one of the cups. Repeat the procedure until each of the teacups has a marble. *Our* job is to calculate the probability that exactly n of the N teacups contain red marbles.

The probability that any *one* cup you care to mention (without peeking) contains a red marble is p. The probability that any array of n cups you chose to designate contains only red marbles is p^n, since the marbles were selected blindly from a vast, well-mixed population. The chance that the *rest* of the cups (those you didn't designate) contain only green marbles is, by the same argument, q^{N-n}. Thus, the probability that any blindly designated array of n teacups contains only red marbles while the remainder contain only green is $p^n q^{N-n}$.

If we can now figure out how many different arrays of n teacups can be designated, we've got our answer. That answer will be

$$P_n = p^n q^{N-n} \times \text{the number of different arrays of } n \text{ teacups that can be selected from an array of } N \text{ cups.}$$

So, pick a cup! You have N choices available, and thus any one of N cups can be your choice. Whatever the outcome of that choice, there are $N - 1$ cups remaining, and any one of $N - 1$ cups can be your second choice. Therefore, the number of different sequences of n cups that can be drawn is

$$N\,(N-1)\,(N-2)\ldots[N-(n-1)].$$

Many of these sequences, however, may constitute identical arrays of n cups. The sequences shown below, for example, represent identical arrays of designated cups.

First choice	Second choice	Third choice
7	3	1
1	7	3
1	3	7
7	1	3
3	7	1
3	1	7

The number of different arrays of n cups that can be designated is given by

$$\frac{\text{number of different sequences in which } n \text{ cups can be drawn from } N \text{ cups}}{\text{number of different sequences in which } n \text{ cups can be arranged}}$$

In the example above, the first choice can be any one of three cups. Once the first choice is made, the second choice can be either of two. When that is fixed, the last choice is fixed, so that the number of different sequences is given by

$$3 \times 2 \times 1 = 3!$$

In general, for n cups, the number of different sequences is $n!$ The desired number of different arrays, then, is given by

$$\frac{N\,(N-1)\,(N-2)\ldots[N-(n-1)]}{n!}.$$

You should have no trouble showing that this is equivalent to

$$\frac{N!}{(N-n)!\,n!}$$

Q.E.D.

Two special cases of the binomial probability distribution are of outstanding usefulness in genetics. For both of these cases the number of trials, N, is very large. The two cases are distinguished only by their values of p, the probability of success per trial. The Gaussian distribution is a good approximation to the binomial distribution when p is not too small. Further discussion and application of the Gaussian distribution will be found in Brewbaker's *Agricultural Genetics* in this series. In the present volume we have numerous occasions to employ the other special case, the Poisson distribution. When $p << 1$,

$$P_n = \frac{x^n e^{-x}}{n!}$$

where x is the average number of successes in N trials and e is the base of the natural logarithms.

In order to clarify the conditions under which Poisson's expression is an adequate approximation to the binomial probability distribution, we shall "derive" the former from the latter.

One of the definitions of e, the base of the natural logarithms is

$$e = \sum_{r=0}^{\infty} \frac{1}{r!} = \frac{1}{0!} + \frac{1}{1!} + \frac{1}{2!} + \frac{1}{3!} + \frac{1}{4!} + \ldots$$

$$= \frac{1}{1} + \frac{1}{1} + \frac{1}{2 \times 1} + \frac{1}{3 \times 2 \times 1} + \frac{1}{4 \times 3 \times 2 \times 1} + \ldots$$

$$= 1 + 1 + \frac{1}{2} + \frac{1}{6} + \frac{1}{24} + \ldots$$

$$= 2.718 + \ldots$$

Those of you who like the mathematics of infinite series might like to demonstrate that

$$e^{-x} = \sum_{r=0}^{\infty} \frac{(-x)^r}{r!} = \frac{(-x)^0}{0!} + \frac{(-x)^1}{1!} + \frac{(-x)^2}{2!} + \frac{(-x)^3}{3!} + \ldots$$

$$= \frac{1}{1} - \frac{x}{1} + \frac{x^2}{2} - \frac{x^3}{6} + \ldots,$$

or you can accept this series as a *definition* of e^{-x}. The rest is easy.

Let's start with the binomial probability distribution written in the form

$$P_n = \frac{N(N-1)(N-2) \ldots [N-(n-1)]}{n!} p^n (1-p)^{N-n}$$

When $N >> n$,

$$N(N-1)(N-2) \ldots [N-(n-1)] = N \cdot N \cdot N \ldots = N^n$$

When $N >> n$ and $p << 1$,

$$(1-p)^{N-n} = (1-p)^N$$

Now

$$(1-p)^N = 1 - Np + \frac{N(N-1)}{2!} p^2 - \frac{N(N-1)(N-2)}{3!} p^3 + \ldots$$

which, when N is vast,

$$= 1 - Np + \frac{N^2p^2}{2!} - \frac{N^3p^3}{3!} + \ldots$$

$$= e^{-Np}$$

So that, upon substituting the indicated approximate equalities, we get

$$P_n = \frac{N^n}{n!} p^n e^{-Np} = \frac{(Np)^n}{n!} e^{-Np}$$

By definition, $Np = x$, completing the derivation.

References

Feller, William, *An Introduction to Probability Theory and Its Application*, Vol. I. New York: John Wiley and Sons, 1957. "A [beautiful] treatment of probability theory developed in terms of mathematical concepts." Quote from the dust jacket of the second edition with parenthetical comment by F.W.S.

Hodgman, Charles D., Mathematical tables from *Handbook of Chemistry and Physics*. Cleveland: Chemical Rubber Publishing Co. The mathematical tables of the *Handbook* will fit in your pocket. The sections on exponential functions and factorials are useful in problems involving the Poisson distribution, radioactive decay processes, mapping functions, etc.

Problems

A.1. (a) By means of the series definition of e^{-x}, calculate the following to within an accuracy of a few per cent:

$$e^{-1} \qquad e^{-2} \qquad e^{-0.6} \qquad e^{-0.01} \qquad e^{-0.2}$$

(b) In Fig. A.1, plot your values and draw a smooth curve through them.

(c) In Fig. A.2, plot your values again and draw a straight line through them.

(d) From the plot in Fig. A.2, determine the values of

$$e^{-3} \qquad e^{-3.6} \qquad e^{-5} \qquad e^{-0.3}$$

A.2. Consider a bucket containing 10 marbles, 7 of which are red, 3 of which are blue. What is the probability of each of the following samples?

(a) In a sample of size 2, both red.
(b) In a sample of size 2, 1 red and 1 blue.
(c) In a sample of size 5, 3 red and 2 blue.
(d) In a sample of size 5, 4 red and 1 blue.
(e) In a sample of size 9, 7 red and 2 blue.

A.3. (a) Consider a bucket containing an immense number of marbles, 70 per cent of which are red, 30 per cent of which are blue. What is the probability of each of the following samples?

(1) In a sample of size 2, both red.
(2) In a sample of size 5, 3 red and 2 blue.

(3) In a sample of size N, n red and $N - n$ blue.

(b) Consider the bucket to contain 0.9999 red and 0.0001 blue. What is the probability of each of the following samples?

(1) In a sample of size 1,000, the chance of 3 blues.

(2) In a sample of size 10^5, the chance of 6 blues.

(3) In a sample of size 10^4, the chance of no blues.

(c) Consider a bucket containing 2×10^{12} red marbles, 10^{12} blue marbles, and 10^{12} green marbles. Calculate the following probabilities:

(1) In a sample of size 1 drawn randomly from the bucket, the probability of a green marble; of a red marble.

(2) In a sample of size 2, the probability of a blue and a green; of a red and a blue.

(3) In a sample of size 5, the probability of 3 reds.

(4) In a sample of size 6, the probability of 2 greens.

(d) Suppose 10^4 purple marbles are tossed into the bucket in Problem A.3c. Calculate the following probabilities in a sample of size 4×10^8.

(1) The probability of no purple marbles.

(2) The probability of 3 purple marbles.

(3) The probability of 2 or more purple marbles.

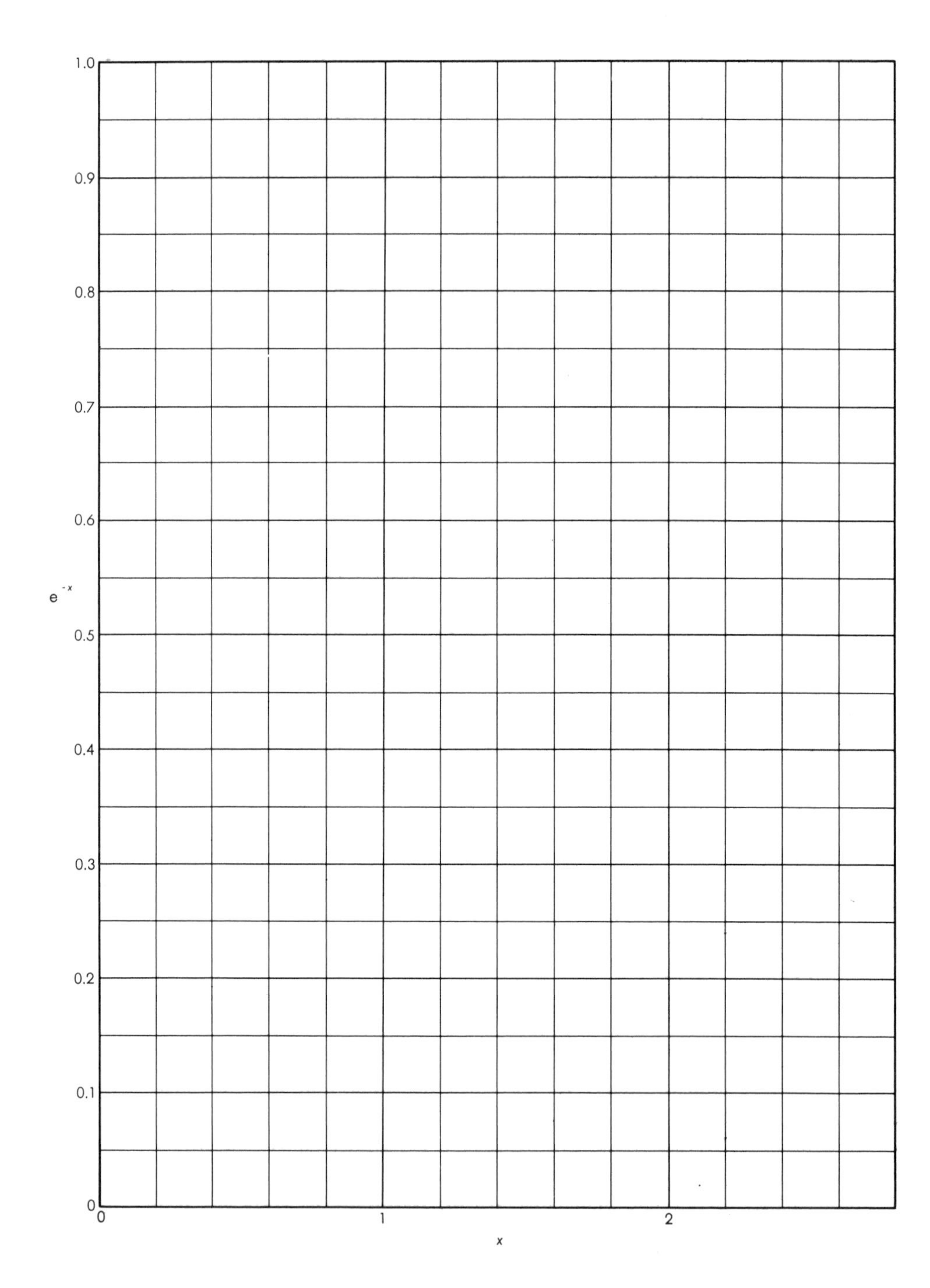

Fig. A.1. A *do-it-yourself* plot of e^{-x} versus x on linear coordinates (see Problem A.1b).

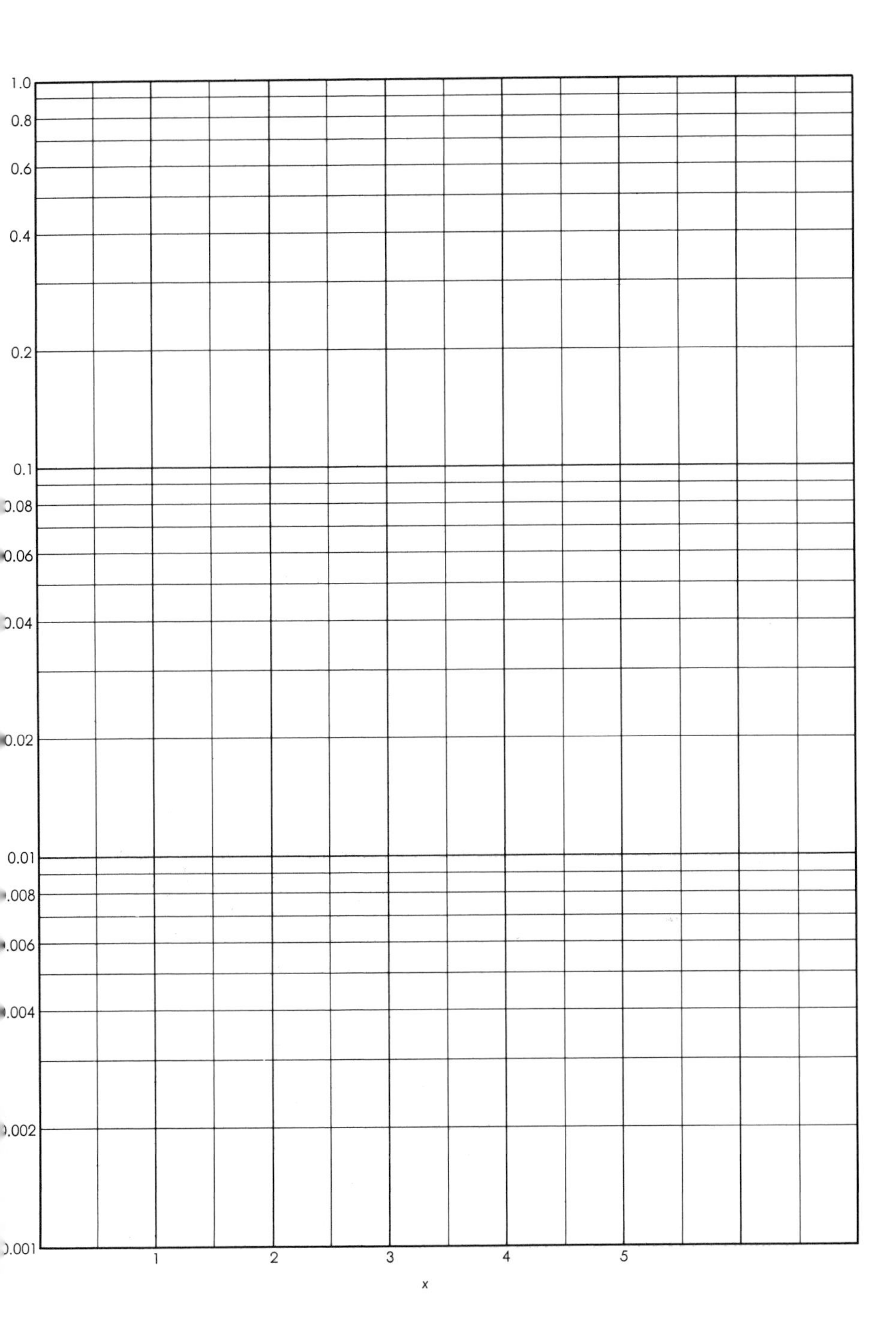

Fig. A.2 A *do-it-yourself* plot of e^{-x} versus x on "semi-logarithmic" coordinates (see Problems A.1c and A.1d). I trust that your points fell on a straight line. When working problems throughout the book, approximate values of e^{-x} can be read from your graph as needed.

Answers to Problems

Chapter One

1.1. 0.45 hours
1.2. 1.74:1
1.3b. 0.72 hours
1.3c. 360
1.3d. 5×10^{-5}
1.4. 500, 250, 125, 125
1.5a. 448
1.5b. 5×10^{-6}
1.6. 7×10^{-9}
1.7a. 2
1.7b. 10^{-8}

Chapter Two

2.1a. 5.7×10^{-7} sec.$^{-1}$
2.1b. 10^{8} atoms
2.2a. 10%
2.2b. 2×10^{-11} micrograms
2.2c. 1.2×10^{7} daltons
2.3a. 4×10^{5} atoms
2.3b. 10^{8} daltons

Chapter Three

3.1a. 111
3.1b. 126
3.1c. 151
3.1d. 135
3.1e. 227
3.1f. 242
3.1g. 267
3.1h. 251
3.1i. 6.6×10^{6}
3.2. not more than 68 μ
3.3. 15,000
3.4. 10^{6021}

Chapter Four

4.1a. 2
4.1b. 2
4.1c. 6
4.1d. all
4.2. The "heavy" DNA is 4% more dense than the "light" DNA.
4.3a. 1 min.
4.3b. 2×10^{5} pairs/min.

Chapter Five

5.1. 5×10^{-5}
5.3a1. 1
5.3a2. 0.16
5.3b1. 1
5.3b2. 10^{-5}
5.3c. 4×10^{-6}
5.4. 10%

Chapter Six

6.1a. 17 min.
6.1b. 30-45 min.
6.2. 3.6×10^4
6.3. 36 min.
6.4a. 2
6.4b1. 0
6.4b2. 4, i.e., a twin
6.4b3. none
6.4b4. 2, i.e., a single
6.4c. 2 singles:1 twin
6.4d. single
6.4e. 2:1
6.4f1. all singles
6.4f2. 10:1
6.4f3. 2:1
6.4g. 2:1

Chapter Seven

7.1a. 2
7.1b. 20
7.1c. $\frac{1}{2}$
7.2b2. 0.22; 29 ideal map units
7.2c2. $S = 0.45$; double recombinant frequency = 0.020
7.3. 37 ideal map units
7.5a. all tetratype
7.5b1. $\frac{2}{3}$
7.5b2. $\frac{2}{3}$, $\frac{2}{3}$, $\frac{2}{3}$; 0, $\frac{2}{3}$, 0
7.6a. 1:1
7.6b. 1
7.6c. $\frac{1}{2}$, $\frac{3}{4}$, $\frac{2}{3}$
7.6d. $\frac{2}{3}$, $\frac{2}{3}$
7.7a. .07
7.7b. 8.6
7.7c. 6.0

Chapter Eight

8.1a. 2.3
8.1b. ∞
8.1c. 0.036
8.1d. 7.55
8.1e. 49%
8.2a. 2.7
8.2b. 0.163; 0.223; 0.315
8.2c. 1.0
8.2d. 0.2; 0.3; 0.5
8.2e. 0.036
8.3f. 1×10^{-4}

Chapter Nine

9.1a. 10^{-6}
9.3a. $\frac{1}{2}$
9.3b. $\frac{1}{3}$, $\frac{1}{3}$, $\frac{1}{3}$, $\frac{1}{12}$
9.4a. *B*
9.4b. *ADC*

Chapter Ten

10.1a. $\frac{1}{2}$

10.1b.

Genotypes	Frequencies
A/A[1]	$\frac{1}{4}$
A/a	$\frac{1}{2}$
a/a	$\frac{1}{4}$

10.1c. $\frac{1}{4}$

[1] The notation A/A means that each of the homologous chromosomes in the diploid carries the allele A at locus 1.

10.1d.

Genotypes	Frequencies of types if loci 1 and 2	
	are unlinked	recombine 20% of the time
AB	$\frac{1}{4}$	0.4
ab	$\frac{1}{4}$	0.4
Ab	$\frac{1}{4}$	0.1
aB	$\frac{1}{4}$	0.1

10.1e.

Phenotypes	Frequencies of types if loci 1 and 2	
	are unlinked	recombine 20% of the time
AB	$\frac{9}{16}$	0.66
Ab	$\frac{3}{16}$	0.09
aB	$\frac{3}{16}$	0.09
ab	$\frac{1}{16}$	0.16

10.1f.

Genotypes	Frequency of type if S is	
	0.6	0
aBd	0.006	0
AbD	0.006	0

10.2a. 3
10.2b. 2–1–4
10.2c. Loci 2 and 1 recombine 40% of the time. Loci 1 and 4 recombine 10% of the time.
10.2d. 0.6
10.3a. 0.20
10.3b. 0.42; 0.01
10.4a. 0.01 and 0.20, respectively
10.4b. 2
10.5. $\frac{1}{2}$

Appendix

A.1a. 0.368; 0.135; 0.549; 0.990; 0.819
A.1d. 0.050; 0.027; 0.0067; 0.74
A.2a. $\frac{42}{90}$
A.2b. $\frac{42}{90}$
A.2c. $\frac{5}{12}$
A.2d. $\frac{5}{12}$
A.2e. $\frac{3}{10}$
A.3a1. 0.49
A.3a2. 0.32
A.3a3. $\frac{N!}{(N-n)\,!n!}\,(0.7)^n(0.3)^{N-n}$
A.3b1. 1.51×10^{-4}
A.3b2. 0.063
A.3b3. 0.368
A.3c1. $\frac{1}{4}$; $\frac{1}{2}$
A.3c2. $\frac{1}{8}$; $\frac{1}{4}$
A.3c3. $\frac{5}{16}$
A.3c4. $\frac{1215}{4096}$
A.3d1. 0.368
A.3d2. 0.061
A.3d3. 0.264

Index

C

D

R

S

T

U

V

W

X

Z